NUMBER 7

New American Review

PUBLISHED BY THE NEW AMERICAN LIBRARY
NEW YORK AND TORONTO · THE NEW ENGLISH
LIBRARY LIMITED, LONDON

NEW AMERICAN REVIEW

EDITOR: THEODORE SOLOTAROFF
POETRY EDITOR: STANLEY MOSS
ASSISTANT EDITOR: NANCY HARDIN
ASSISTANT TO THE EDITOR: MICHAEL SEIDMAN

EDITORIAL COMMITTEE:
Mary Corey Bisson, Edward T. Chase, Nina Finkelstein, Dudley
Frasier, Robert Haynie, Katharine Kidde, Patrick O'Connor,
Jean Read, James Trupin

Art Director: Jim Plumeri
Production Associates: Lee Hockman, Veronica Johnson, Irene
Kask, Terence McCabe
Business Manager: Arthur Tiger

Cover designed by Plumeri/De Simone

First Printing, August, 1969

Library of Congress Catalog Card Number: 67–27377

NEW AMERICAN REVIEW is published in the United
States by The New American Library, Inc., 1301 Avenue of the
Americas, New York, New York 10019; in Canada by The New
American Library of Canada Limited, 295 King Street East, To-
ronto 2, Ontario; in the United Kingdom by The New English
Library Limited, Barnard's Inn, Holborn, London, E.C. 1, Eng-
land · Copyright © 1969 by The New American Library, Inc.
· All rights reserved · Printed in the United States of America ·

The editors invite submissions. Manuscripts will not be returned
unless accompanied by stamped, self-addressed envelope.

NAR This issue inaugurates our new correspondence department which contains, alas, only one letter. It is written by Ellen Willis, who contributed the much praised "Lessons of Chicago" to *NAR #6* and who charges that my preliminary remarks placed her essay in a false context and misrepresented its thrust. I don't agree with the latter, as I don't agree with some of Miss Willis' other views such as "good writing is counterrevolutionary," a statement that would seem merely callow if its history didn't have so much blood on it. Be that as it may, it's easy enough for a writer to feel misrepresented by having his contribution summarily pushed into a context of the editor's choosing; and since I haven't much enjoyed the job of introducing each issue in this way, it seems well to stop doing so and to let *NAR #7* and its writers speak for themselves. Instead, I'd like to use the few pages we have left over to talk about some matters related to the evolving character of *NAR* as an American journal.

A few months ago the editors of *Harper's Magazine* announced that they would no longer accept unsolicited manuscripts. No doubt they had their good and sufficient reasons; one of which, I imagine, is that their decision confirms rather than alters their actual practice of acquiring material. Still, the decision strikes me as unfortunate since it indicates a further shrinkage of the open market for good writing and acts as a fresh discouragement to writers, particularly the young and obscure, who will have another reason to believe that the game is rigged for the well-known or the well-connected. Of course, there are some writers who couldn't care less, who have justifiably given up on "the Establishment" and its journals and who rely on the little magazines to sustain their work, if not themselves. But there are also many writers who look upon the few good national magazines as both a beacon and a point of arrival for their writing careers and who find themselves caught in the gap between, say, *Kayak, December,* or *For Now,* on the one hand, and *Esquire, The New Yorker,* or *Harper's* on the other.

To be sure, one hears that the New York marketplace is booming and that some editors and agents comb the prestigious writing workshops and little magazines like football scouts visit Notre Dame or Grambling. But the fact remains that power and influence steadily accumulate at one end of the literary scene. That a magazine like *Playboy* comes out of Chicago merely points up the fact that you don't have to publish in New York to set up your editorial muse on Madison Avenue. Another and sadder example of this is the first issue of the "new" *Antioch Review,* formerly one of the more astute of the university quarterlies. Dealing with current magazines, the issue leads off with some knowing shoptalk by the editor of *New York Magazine,* paying particular tribute to *Esquire,* as he should, and goes on to imitate his standards of journalism, as *Antioch* shouldn't. Who needs a little magazine version of "the new journalism"? Perhaps it's the temporary mistake of a new editor, but in such ways does the urbanity of New York, much of it pure vinyl, become the national style of consciousness, infiltrating even into places that formerly resisted it.

If New York were the genuine center of American creativity such as Paris, Vienna, and London once were of their respective nations, its authority might be justifiable. But it is not and it never has been, except possibly for a period early in the century. The native genius of American writing, like that of its music and art, has been a thoroughly decentralized and mobile one, and even when it has appeared to settle in one area or among one group of writers, it has never abided there for very long. It may have been in New England for a time and then in the frontier states; or, in more recent times, in the Middle West, and then in the South, and then among the urban minorities. Each of these were fresh territories in which it renewed itself, new vistas of American character, milieus, and values in a mysteriously huge and diverse continent of possibilities. If most books were published in New York or Boston, these cities were merely the points of transmission, the relay stations of the national dream of cultural opportunity which was like Gatsby's dream on his Long Island estate, one that was "already behind him, somewhere back in that vast obscurity behind the city, where the dark fields of the republic

(continued on p. 222)

CONTENTS

Sexual Politics: Miller, Mailer, and Genet*

Kate Millett

I

I WOULD ASK HER to prepare the bath for me. She would pretend to demur but she would do it just the same. One day, while I was seated in the tub soaping myself, I noticed that she had forgotten the towels. "Ida," I called, "bring me some towels!" She walked into the bathroom and handed me them. She had on a silk bathrobe and a pair of silk hose. As she stooped over the tub to put the towels on the rack her bathrobe slid open. I slid to my knees and buried my head in her muff. It happened so quickly that she didn't have time to rebel or even to pretend to rebel. In a moment I had her in the tub, stockings and all. I slipped the bathrobe off and threw it on the floor. I left the stockings on—it made her more lascivious looking, more the Cranach type. I lay back and pulled her on top of me. She was just like a bitch in heat, biting me all over, panting, gasping, wriggling like a worm on the hook. As we were drying ourselves she bent over and began nibbling at my prick. I sat on the edge of the tub and she kneeled at my feet gobbling it. After a while I made her stand up, bend over; then I let her have it from the rear. She had a small juicy cunt, which fitted me like a glove. I bit the nape of her neck, the lobes of her ears, the sensitive spot on her shoulder, and as I pulled away I left the mark of my teeth on her beautiful white ass. Not a word spoken.

This colorful, descriptive prose is taken from Henry Miller's celebrated *Sexus*, first published in Paris in the forties but outlawed from the sanitary shores of his native America until the recent Grove edition. Miller, alias Val, is recounting his seduction of Ida Verlaine, the wife of his friend Bill Woodruff. As an account of sexual passage, the excerpt has much in it of note beyond that merely biological activity which the narrator would call "fucking." Indeed, it is just this other content which gives the representation of the incident its value and character.

First one must consider the circumstances and the context of the scene. Val has just met Bill Woodruff outside a burlesque theater where Ida Verlaine is performing. In the rambling fashion of Miller's narrative, this meeting calls up the memory of the hero's sexual bouts with Ida ten years before, whereupon follow eleven pages of vivid reenactment. First, there is Ida herself:

> She was just exactly the way her name sounded—pretty, vain, theatrical, faithless, spoiled, pampered, petted. Beautiful as a Dresden doll, only she had raven tresses and a Javanese slant to her soul. If she had a soul at all! Lived entirely in the body, in her senses, her desires— and she directed the show, the body show, with her tyrannical little will which poor Woodruff translated as some monumental force of character. . . . Ida swallowed everything like a pythoness. She was heartless and insatiable.

Woodruff himself is given out as a uxorious fool: "The more he did for her the less she cared for him. She was a monster from head to toe." The narrator claims to be utterly immune to Ida's power but is nonetheless subject to coldly speculative curiosity:

> I just didn't give a fuck for her, as a person, though I often wondered what she might be like as a piece of fuck, so to speak. I wondered about it in a detached way, but somehow it got across to her, got under her skin.

As a friend of the family, Val is entitled to spend the night at the Woodruff house, followed by breakfast in bed while husband Bill goes off to work. Val's initial tactic of extracting service from Ida is important to the events which follow:

She hated the thought of waiting on me in bed. She didn't do it for her husband and she couldn't see why she should do it for me. To take breakfast in bed was something I never did except at Woodruff's place. I did it expressly to annoy and humiliate her.

In accord with one of the myths at the very heart of a Miller novel, the protagonist, who is always some version of the author himself, is sexually irresistible and potent to an almost mystic degree. It is therefore no very great surprise to the reader that Ida falls into his hands. To return to the picking, then, and the passage quoted at length above. The whole scene reads very much like a series of stratagems, aggressive on the part of the hero and acquiescent on the part of what custom forces us to designate as the heroine of the episode. His first maneuver, for example, is to coerce further service in the form of a demand for towels, which reduces Ida to the appropriate roles of a hostess and a domestic. That Ida has dressed herself in a collapsible bathrobe and silk stockings is not only accommodating, but almost romance-like. The female reader may realize that one rarely wears stockings without the assistance of a girdle or garter belt, but classic masculine fantasy dictates that nudity's most appropriate exception is some gauze-like material, be it hosiery or underwear.

VAL MAKES the first move: "I slid to my knees and buried my head in her muff." The locution "muff" is significant because it is a clue to the reader that the putative humility of the action and the stance of petition it implies are not to be taken at face value. "Muff" carries the tone, implicit in the whole passage, of one male relating an exploit to another male in the masculine vocabulary and with its point of view. What is considerably more revealing of the actual character of the action is the comment which follows: "It happened so quickly she didn't have time to rebel or even to pretend to rebel." Since the entire scene is a description not so much of sexual intercourse, but rather of intercourse in the service of power, "rebel" is a highly charged word. Val had already informed the reader that "she wanted to bring me under her spell, make me walk the tight-rope, as she had done with Woodruff and her other suitors." The issue, of course, is which of the two is to walk a tightrope, who shall be master?

Having immediately placed Ida under his domination, Val acts fast to forestall insubordination. This prompts the next remarkable event—Val brings her into his element, as it were, and places her in the distinctly ridiculous position of being in a bathtub with her clothes on. Again the language indicates the underlying issue of power: "I had her in the bathtub." The reader is also advised that credit should be given to the narrator for his speed and agility; Ida is swooshed into the tub in a trice. Having assumed all initiative, Val then proceeds to divest his prey of her redundant bathrobe and throw it on the floor.

The display of stockings and nudity is brought forward for aesthetic delectation; it contributes to make Ida "more lascivious looking, more the Cranach type." The frail perfection of a Cranach nude had been mentioned earlier as Ida's comparable body type. Juxtaposing the innocence and rarity of this image with the traditional "girlie" figure in silk stockings is an eminent bit of strategy. The word "lascivious" implies a deliberate sensuality and is dependent upon a relish for the prurient, and particularly for the degrading, in sexual activity, which, in its turn, relies on the distinctly puritanical conviction that sexuality is indeed dirty and faintly ridiculous. Webster defines "lascivious" as "wanton; lewd; lustful" or a "tendency to produce lewd emotions." The Cranach in question is most likely to be the delicate and rather morbid Eve of the Genesis Panel, now depreciated to a calendar girl.

Val proceeds—his manner coolly self-assured and redolent of comfort: "I lay back and pulled her on top of me." What follows is purely subjective description. Ceasing to admire himself, the hero is now lost in wonder at his effects. For the fireworks which ensue are Ida's, though produced by a Pavlovian mechanism. Like the famous programmed dog, in fact "just like a bitch in heat," Ida responds to the protagonist's skilled manipulation: ". . . biting me all over, panting, gasping, wriggling like a worm on the hook." No evidence is ever offered to the reader of any such animal-like failure of self-restraint in the response of our hero. It is he who is the hook, and she who is the worm: the implication is clearly one of steely self-composure contrasted to lower-life servility and larval vulnerability. Ida has—in the double, but related, meaning of the phrase—been had.

In the conventional order of this genre of sexual narrative, one position of intercourse must rapidly be followed by another less orthodox and therefore of greater interest. Miller obliges the reader with a quick instance of dorsal intercourse, preceded by a flitting interlude of fellatio. But more pertinent to the larger issues under investigation is the information that Ida is now so "hooked" that it is she who makes the first move: ". . . she bent over and began nibbling at my prick." The hero's "prick," now very centerstage, is still a hook and Ida metamorphosed into a very gullible fish. (Perhaps all of this aquatic imagery was inspired by the bathtub.)

Furthermore, positions are significantly reversed: "I sat on the edge of the tub and she kneeled at my feet gobbling it." The power nexus is clearly outlined. It remains only for the hero to assert his victory by the arrogance of his final gesture: "After a while I made her stand up, bend over; then I let her have it from the rear."

What the reader is vicariously experiencing at this juncture is a nearly supernatural sense of power—should the reader be a male. For the passage is not only a vivacious and imaginative use of circumstance, detail, and context to evoke the excitations of sexual intercourse, it is also a male assertion of dominance over a weak, compliant, and rather unintelligent female. It is a case of sexual politics at the fundamental level of copulation. Several satisfactions for hero and reader alike undoubtedly accrue upon this triumph of the male ego, the most tangible one being communicated in the following: "She had a small juicy cunt which fitted me like a glove."

The hero then caters to the reader's appetite in telling how he fed upon his object, biting ". . . the nape of her neck, the lobes of her ears, the sensitive spot on her shoulder, and as I pulled away I left the mark of my teeth on her beautiful white ass." The last bite is almost a mark of patent to denote possession and use, but further still, to indicate attitude. Val had previously informed us that Bill Woodruff was so absurd and doting a groveler that he had demeaned himself to kiss this part of his wife's anatomy. Our hero adjusts the relation of the sexes by what he believes is a more correct gesture.

Without question the most telling statement in the narrative is its last sentence: "Not a word spoken." Like the folk hero who never condescended to take off his hat, Val has accomplished the entire campaign, including its *coup de grace*, without stooping to one word of human communication.

THE RECOLLECTION of the affair continues for several more pages of diversified stimulation by which the hero now moves to consolidate his position of power through a series of physical and emotional gestures of contempt. In answer to her question ". . . you don't really like me, do you?" he replies with studied insolence, "'I like *this*,' said I giving her a stiff jab." His penis is now an instrument of chastisement, whereas Ida's genitalia are but the means of her humiliation: "I like your cunt, Ida . . . it's the best thing about you."

All further representations conspire to convince the reader of Val's superior intelligence and control, while demonstrating the female's moronic complaisance and helpless carnality; each moment exalts him further and degrades her lower: a dazzling instance of the sexual double standard:

> "You never wear any undies do you? You're a slut, do you know it?"
> I pulled her dress up and made her sit that way while I finished my coffee.
> "Play with it a bit while I finish this."
> "You're filthy," she said, but she did as I told her.
> "Take your two fingers and open it up. I like the color of it."
> . . . With this I reached for a candle on the dresser at my side and I handed it to her.
> "Let's see if you can get it in all the way . . ."
> "You can make me do anything, you dirty devil."
> "You like it, don't you?"

Val's imperious aptitude sets the tone for the dramatic events which follow, and the writing soars off into that species of fantasy which Steven Marcus calls "pornotopic," a shower of orgasms:

> I laid her on a small table and when she was on the verge of exploding I picked her up and walked around the room with her; then I took it out and made her walk on her hands holding her by the thighs, letting it slip out now and then to excite her still more.

In both the foregoing selections the most operative verbal phrases are: "I laid her on a small table" (itself a pun), "made her walk on her hands," "She did as I told her," and "I pulled her dress up and made her sit that way." Ida is putty, even less substantial than common clay, and like a bullied child is continually taking orders for activity which in the hero's view degrades her while it aggrandizes him.

Meanwhile, the hero's potency is so superb and overwhelming that he is lost in admiration: "It went on like this until I had such an erection that even after I shot a wad into her it stayed up like a hammer. That excited her terribly." And emerging from his efforts covered with so much credit and satisfaction, he takes account of his assets: "My cock looked like a bruised rubber hose; it hung between my legs, extended an inch or two beyond its normal length and swollen beyond recognition."

Ida, who has never demanded much of his attention, nor of ours, is quickly forgotten as the hero goes off to feast in his inimitable adolescent fashion: "I went to the drug store and swallowed a couple of malted milks." His final pronouncement on his adventure also redounds to his credit: "A royal bit of fucking, thought I to myself, wondering how I'd act when I met Woodruff again." Royal indeed.

During the course of the episode, Val obliges the reader with intelligence of the Woodruffs' marital incompatibility, a misalliance of a curiously physical character. Mr. Woodruff possesses a genital organ of extraordinary proportions, "a veritable horse cock." "I remember the first time I saw it—I could scarcely believe my eyes" whereas Mrs. Woodruff's dimensions have already been referred to under the rubric "small juicy cunt." But lest this irreconcilable misfortune in any way excuse her in seeking out other satisfaction, it is repeatedly underlined, throughout the section of the novel where she figures, that she is an uppity woman. Therefore the hero's exemplary behavior in reducing her to the status of a mere female. Moreover, we are given to understand that she is an insatiable nymphomaniac—thus his wit and prosperity in discovering and exploiting her.

THE FIGURE OF Ida Verlaine appears to have haunted Miller's imagination. It is not enough that his hero should discover her "whorish" nature and bring her to paroxysms of sensual capitulation while congratulating himself on cuckolding her adulating husband. In an earlier work, *Black Spring*, she appears as a woman discovered at prostitution and properly chastised. Here Miller's didactic nature obtrudes itself and one is made to perceive the validity of his claim that his is a deeply moral imagination.

Bill Woodruff's brilliant reaction when the news is passed along to him by another buddy is narrated at length and with obvious relish. The narrator, again a version of Miller, regards the anecdote as "cute":

This night, however, he waited up for her and when she came sailing in, chipper, perky, a little lit up and cold as usual he pulled her up short with a "where were you to-night?" She tried pulling her usual yarn, of course. "Cut that," he said. "I want you to get your things off and tumble into bed." That made her sore. She mentioned in her roundabout way that she didn't want any of that business. "You don't feel in the mood for it, I suppose," says he, and then he adds: "that's fine because now I'm going to warm you up a bit." With that he up and ties her to the bedstead, gags her, and then goes for the razor strop. On the way to the bathroom, he grabs a bottle of mustard from the kitchen. He comes back with the razor strop and he belts the piss out of her. And after that he rubs the mustard into the raw welts. "That ought to keep you warm for to-night," he says. And so saying he makes her bend over and spread her legs apart.

"Now," he says, "I'm going to pay you as usual," and taking a bill out of his pocket he crumbles it and then shoves it up her quim.

Miller concludes the saga of Ida and Bill with a last joke at the cuckold's expense, for Bill is still a cuckold, and a maxim for the reader, in capital letters, is put forward as "the purpose of all this"—merely, "To prove what has not yet been demonstrated, namely that

THE GREAT ARTIST IS HE WHO CONQUERS THE ROMANTIC IN HIMSELF."

Miller's educational intentions in the passage are abundantly clear. Females who are frigid, e.g. not sexually compliant, should be beaten. Females who break the laws of marital fidelity should also be beaten, for the barter system of marriage (sex in return for security) must not be violated by outside commerce. Rather more informative than this sober doctrine of the cave is the insight it provides into Miller's sexual/literary motives and their undeniably sadistic overtones. They are closer to the vicarious politic of the cock-pit than of the boudoir, but the latter often casts considerable light on the former.

II

"I HAVE NOTHING in me," she said. "Do we go ahead?"

"Who knows," I said, "keep quiet."

And I could feel her beginning to come. The doubt in me had tipped her off, the adjuration to be quiet had thrown the bolt. She was a minute away, but she was on her way, and just as if one of her wily fingers had thrown some switch in me, I was gone like a bat and shaking hands with the Devil once more. Rare greed shone in her eyes, pleasure in her mouth, she was happy. I was ready to chase, I was gorged to throw the first spill, high on a choice, like some cat caught on two wires I was leaping back and forth, in separate runs for separate strokes, bringing spoils and secrets up to the Lord from the red mills, bearing messages of defeat back from that sad womb, and then I chose—ah, but there was time to change—I chose her cunt. It was no graveyard now, no warehouse, no, more like a chapel now, a modest decent place, but its walls were snug, its odor was green, there was a sweetness in the chapel, a muted reverential sweetness in those wall of stone. "That is what prison will be like for you," said a last effort of my inner tongue. "Stay here!" came a command from inside of me; except that I could feel the Devil's meal beneath, its fires were lifting through the floor, and I waited for the warmth to reach inside, to come up from the cellar below, to bring booze and heat up and licking tongues, I was up above a choice which would take me on one wind or another, and I had to give myself, I could not hold back, there was an explosion, furious, treacherous and hot as the gates of an icy slalom with the speed at my heels overtaking my nose. I had one of those splittings of a second where the senses fly out and there in that instant the itch reached into me and drew me out and I jammed up her ass and came as if I'd been flung across the room. She let out a cry of rage.

The foregoing is a description of heterosexual sodomy from Norman Mailer's *An American Dream*. The practice is not only one of the book's primary attractions, it is so central to the action that one might even say the plot depended on it. Mailer's hero, Stephen Rojack, has just finished murdering his wife and is now relieving his feelings by buggering his maid.

Mailer transparently identifies with his hero, who has little motive for the killing beyond the fact that he is unable to "master" his mate by any means short of murder. The desire for such mastery is perfectly understandable to Mailer and even engages his sympathy. So does Rojack's surprisingly old-fashioned stance of the outraged husband. Mrs. Rojack, to whom Mr. Rojack's many affairs are perfectly well known, has found the temerity to advise him that since separation she too has indulged herself. Moreover, and here is where one must depend on the forceful role of sodomy in the book, she admits that she has been enjoying this very activity with her new lovers. Now sodomy is a specialty in which our hero takes personal pride. Though he boasts to her face that his mistresses far excel her in this activity, the notion that his wife is committing sodomous adultery is evidently too severe a trial on his patience. It is the final blow to his vanity, his sense of property, and, most material of all, his fancied masculine birthright of superordination, and he promptly retaliates by strangling the upstart. As Mrs. Rojack is one of those Celtic sporting women, it is not easy work and Rojack is exhausted when he finishes—and all the more triumphant: "I was weary with a most honorable fatigue, and my flesh seemed new. I had not felt so nice since I was twelve. It seemed inconceivable at this instant that anything in life could fail to please."

Now to get back to the maid. Rojack had entered her room to find her busily masturbating, surely a fortuitous circumstance. The rest is easy. He calmly removes her hand from her genitals and replaces it with his bare foot "drawing up on the instant out of her a wet spicy wisdom of all the arts and crafts of getting along in the world." The comment is indicative of the heavy heuristic value which the hero is to obtain from his sexual exploits. For an instant Rojack toys with the idea of simply murdering the maid—"I was ready to kill her easy as not, there was an agreeable balance in the thought that I was ready to kill anyone at this moment"—but he decides instead to take her on. Three pages of sexual activity then follow before a word is spoken; and, as the hero boasts, "it must have been five minutes before I chose to give her a kiss, but I took her mouth at last." In doing so, he undertakes to absorb her soul, which is that of a German proletarian. It appears that Mr. Rojack's employee smells, and it is chiefly through her odor that Rojack, a Harvard man, a college professor, a United States congressman, a television personality, and the very recent widower of a rich woman, stumbles upon the understanding outlined in the next statement.

But then, as abruptly as an arrest, a thin high constipated smell (a smell which spoke of rocks and grease and the sewer-damp of wet stones in poor European alleys) came needling its way out of her. She was hungry, and it could have spoiled my pleasure except that there was something intoxicating in the sheer narrow pitch of the smell, so strong, so stubborn, so private, it was a smell which could be mellowed only by the gift of furs and gems.

Though her patron, Rojack is almost too repelled to continue: "it could have spoiled my pleasure." Then he decides that even this unworthy creature can serve him in some way: "I had a desire to skip the sea and mine the earth, a pure prong of desire to bugger, there was canny hard-packed evil in that butt, that I knew."

It is at this point that the first word is spoken; the servant resists the will of her master. But Ruta's "*verboten*" makes little impression on Rojack. He has convinced himself that her essence lies in her rectum and that it is a quality which might be convenient to him. As a newly arrived homicide, he is in immediate need of a bit of that canny lower-class self-preservation Ruta is presumed to contain. For if nothing else, she has the invaluable "knowledge of a city rat." Furthermore, Rojack regards himself in the light of a moralist in search of wisdom and Ruta's anus can teach him about evil.

How evil resides in her bowels or why Ruta has a greater share of it than her master may appear difficult to explain, but many uncanny things are possible with our author. In most of Mailer's fiction sexuality has such a mystical and metaphysical import that genitals acquire definite personalities. Ruta's "box," as Rojack refers to it, has very little to offer; nothing resides therein but "cold gasses from the womb and a storehouse of disappointments." In *An American Dream* female sexuality is depersonalized to the point of being a matter of class or a matter of nature. Ruta behaves like a guttersnipe, Deborah, the former Mrs. Rojack, like a cruel duchess. Cherry, the mistress Rojack later wins, has the virtues of nature, unavailable to poor Ruta, and excelling those of the privileged female who is now too dangerously insubordinate to stay alive. As the hero and a male, Rojack, of course, transcends any such typology.

FINDING WHERE Ruta's true serviceability lies, the hero disdains her vagina to continue rooting in her nether orifice. (Her name appears to be a cruel English pun on this: in German, *"Rute,"* pronounced nearly the same as Ruta, refers both to the switch or birch of chastisement as well as to the penis, and perhaps more than mere linguistic coincidence is involved.) As her resistance renders her difficult to penetrate, Rojack hits upon the device of pulling her hair, noting with fastidious justification that, anyway, it is dyed red: "I could feel the pain in her scalp strain like a crowbar the length of her body and push up the trap, and I was in, that quarter-inch more was gained, the rest was easy." As further justification for his inquiry into her he resorts again to the odor of her presumably vicious, but now fascinating, character:

> What a subtle smell came from her then, something back of the ambition, the narrow stubbornness, the monomaniacal determination to get along in the world, no, that was replaced by something tender as the flesh but not as clean, something sneaky, full of fear.

Just as homicide produced an honorable fatigue in him, Rojack now hits on the glittering idea that in forcibly buggering his servant he is actually performing an act of patriotism because Ruta is a "Nazi." The reader may have some difficulty in accepting this; twenty-three years old and therefore a child during the war, Ruta is hardly a fit subject for Rojack's instant justice. But the hero continues to take an uncommon satisfaction in his racial revenge: "There was a high private pleasure in plugging a Nazi, there was something clean despite all—I felt as if I were gliding in the clear air about Luther's jakes." And through this shift, Rojack, a wizard at manipulative ethics, arrives at a position of moral leverage for any further exploits.

Sodomy has a number of possible meanings in Rojack's mind: homosexuality (he confesses to Cherry that he has some doubts about his heterosexual vocation); a forbidden species of sexuality at which he is an expert and over which he holds copyright; or anal rape, which is his way of expressing contemptuous mastery. It is the acting out of this last attitude which is reserved for Ruta.

Throughout the rest of the passage, Rojack entertains the reader with his contrasting impressions of Ruta's rectum, "a bank of pleasures," and her vagina, "a deserted warehouse, that empty tomb." But this virtuosity is accomplished with certain misgivings. As one might expect, these have nothing to do with her pleasure, which is never the issue, but with Rojack's peculiar notion of sexual honor. After all, he muses, her womb might contain "one poor flower growing in a gallery." Because he has deprived her of the opportunity to bear his seed, a substance Rojack regards with reverential awe, he feels obliged to regard himself as a "great thief." Later he will indulge in a number of "might have beens" about the ill fortune of "that empty womb," that "graveyard which gambled a flower and lost." The fact that his precious semen has been discharged in her rectum and not in her cervix is a source of bemusement, not uncomfortably experienced as guilt. Ruta has missed the radiant opportunity to be impregnated by a higher power and he can only pity her: "I had thought then of what had been left in her. It was perishing in the kitchens of the Devil." And then he wonders: "Was its curse on me? . . . Was that the cloud of oppression which had come to me in the dark? That the seed was expiring in the wrong field?" Perhaps it is this monomania about his own sexual discharge that has made Rojack a specialist in existential dread.

As for Ruta, she responds magically, just as the relevant masculine fantasy dictates. Indeed, her gratitude at being sodomized is positively astonishing: "I do not know why you have trouble with your wife. You are absolutely a genius, Mr. Rojack." Accordingly, the final stages in which this man has his will with his maid take place under the most compliant conditions. Ruta now responds quite as masculine egotism would prescribe: ". . . she was becoming mine as no woman ever had, she wanted to be part of my will." It would seem that she could want nothing better for herself, and at once her "feminine," or again "true woman," instincts emerge and she acquires what her master relays to be ". . . the taste of power in her eyes and mouth, that woman's look that the world is theirs." This delusion of success is, of course, most advantageous to her lord's purposes.

Sexual congress in a Mailer novel is always a matter of strenuous endeavor, rather like mountain climbing—a straining ever upward after achievement. In this, as in so many ways, Mailer is authentically American. Rojack is presently doing very well at his cliff-face, but Ruta begins to waver. She turns with guilty admission of possible failure, "a little look of woe was on her face, a puckered fearful little nine-year-old afraid of her punishment, wishing to be good." In his vast composure, Rojack orders her to "keep quiet." Not only is he more conscious than she of the state of her orgasm, he enjoys a complacent sadistic awareness of what "punishment" might ensue, if she isn't "good."

WHAT FOLLOWS is the passage I have quoted at the outset, almost exclusively a description of Rojack's activity—and properly so—as the coitus is simply his accomplishment as enacted upon Ruta, and therefore its value is precisely its value to him. Very much a solo flight, it is by no means inappropriate that the imagery employed is aeronautic, "I was gone like a bat," etc. It is also a summary of Rojack's major interests: sport—"I was ready to chase," "leaping back and forth in separate runs for separate strokes," "an icy slalom with the speed at my heels"; alcohol—"to bring booze and heat up and licking tongues"; and religion.

By now it is hardly surprising that his orgasm should take on cosmic and metaphysical implications: "a choice which would take me on one wind or another," "one of those splittings of a second where the senses fly out" and give rise to visions of a "huge city in some desert, was it a place on the moon?" What is more noteworthy are the elaborate configurations in the act of the Lord and the Devil. The Devil is manifestly an anal force. The Lord smiles upon Rojack's high mission to fertilize the humble and bring the "spoils and secrets" of his semen to the "sad womb" of this lowly woman through the favor of his visitation. Indeed, Ruta's "cunt," as Rojack calls it, has prospered through association with him and has grown more worthy: "It was no graveyard now, no warehouse, no, more like a chapel now." But despite the purloined phrases from William Blake it is still no great shakes, simply ". . . a modest, decent place, but its walls were snug," and appropriately, it is aware of its exalted, if only sporadic, honor in housing Rojack himself, who deigns to find

in it "a muted reverential sweetness." But having defined
the organ in question in terms of several types of public
buildings, Rojack finally comes to detect in it a prison with
"walls of stone."

The result of this discovery is that, at the last moment,
he escapes back to the free-wheeling Devil of sodomy. The
chief function of this passage is to provide a way for Rojack to commit his crime a second time in symbolic circumstances. Given the often emphasized choice between
the Devil (sodomy) and the Lord (procreation), or death
and life, Rojack once again opts for death. Just as he re-
fuses what we are asked to believe is a portentous existential opportunity to sweeten Ruta's womb with his mag-
ical semen (infallible in its power to bring about conception),
so too does Rojack refuse the choice of acknowledging his
crime, accepting responsibility for it and going to prison.
Ruta's vagina has constituted his foretaste of prison, " 'That
is what prison will be like for you' said a last effort on my
inner tongue. 'Stay here!' came a command from inside of
me." But the Devil has more exotic and dynamic attractions. Rojack claims that he is compelled to his decision
and he explains it in terms of a generosity which pertains
only to himself: "I had to give myself, I could not hold
back." Ruta and prison must do without the hallowed presence of the hero so that Rojack may have his ultimate satisfaction: "I jammed up her ass and came as if I'd been
flung across the room. She let out a cry of rage." It seems
that Mailer is both a romantic manichean and a romantic
diabolist.

AFTER RECEIVING his servant's congratulations on his
dazzling performance, Rojack proceeds calmly to the next
floor and throws his wife's body out of the window. He
has elected to remain with the Devil and stay alive. Ruta
has been a vessel of considerable utility. Through her, or
rather through her "ass," the hero has made his major
decision: to pass the murder off as an accident. And as
Ruta was compliant to an outlandish degree, so is the rest
of the world. All obstacles melt before Rojack who here-
after is a miracle of tough dispatch. Once almost a "loser,"

he is rejuvenated and remade through the act of murder: he wins a fight with a black gangster who cowers before him, a fortune at the tables at Las Vegas, and the love of a nightclub singer who wants him to make her a lady (the last detail a fatuity which is better passed over in silence). Even the police look on Rojack with eyes blinded by admiring camaraderie, and he is permitted to escape to Yucatan. In fact, Mailer's *An American Dream* is an exercise in how to kill your wife and be happy ever after. The reader is given to understand that by murdering one woman and buggering another, Rojack became a "man."

The humanist convictions which underlie *Crime and Punishment* (the original and still the greatest study in what it is like to commit murder), may all go by the board. Both Dostoyevsky and Dreiser, in *An American Tragedy*, gradually created in their murderers an acceptance of responsibility for the violation of life which their actions had constituted, and both transcend their crimes through atonement. Rojack has some singularity in being one of the first literary characters to get away with murder; he is surely the first hero as homicide to rejoice in his crime and never really lose his creator's support. In *Native Son* Richard Wright understood Bigger Thomas's crime while never condoning it and made of it a prototypical fable of the logic of rage in a racist society. Mailer also appears to find in Rojack a symbolic figure whose crime is diagnostic of conditions in American society. But the condition appears to be simply a hostility between the sexes so bitter that it has reached the proportions of a war waged in terms of murder and sodomy. And Mailer is to be on the winning side, to which end he has created in Rojack the last warrior for a curious cause, none other than male supremacy. Rojack is a far cry from Wright's underdog from a Chicago slum acting only through desperation in a novel that is both a plea for racial justice and a threatening vision of what may come to pass should the hope of it fail. Rojack belongs to the oldest ruling class in the world, and like one of Faulkner's ancient retainers of a lost cause, he is making his stand on the preservation of a social hierarchy that sees itself as threatened with extinction. His Jewish ancestry and his "liberal" views to the contrary, Rojack is the last surviving white man as conquering hero. Mailer's *An American Dream* is a rallying cry for a sexual politics in which diplomacy has failed and war is the last political resort of a ruling caste that feels its position in deadly peril.

III

A FEW DAYS LATER, when I met him near the docks Armand ordered me to follow him. Almost without speaking, he took me to his room. With the same apparent scorn he subjected me to his pleasure.

Dominated by his strength and age, I gave the work my utmost care. Crushed by that mass of flesh, which was devoid of the slightest spirituality, I experienced the giddiness of finally meeting the perfect brute, indifferent to my happiness. I discovered the sweetness that could be contained in a thick fleece on torso, belly and thighs and what force it could transmit. I finally let myself be buried in that stormy night. Out of gratitude or fear I placed a kiss on Armand's hairy arm.

"What's eating you? Are you nuts or something?"

"I didn't do any harm."

I remained at his side in order to serve his nocturnal pleasure. When he went to bed, Armand whipped his leather belt from the loops of his trousers and made it snap. It was flogging an invisible victim, a shape of transparent flesh. The air bled. If he frightened me then, it was because of his powerlessness to be the Armand I see, who is heavy and mean. The snapping accompanied and supported him. His rage and despair at not being *him* made him tremble like a horse subdued by darkness, made him tremble more and more. He would not, however, have tolerated my living idly. He advised me to prowl around the station or the zoo and pick up customers. Knowing the terror inspired in me by his person, he didn't deign to keep any eye on me. The money I earned I brought back intact.

This quotation, from Jean Genet's autobiographical novel *The Thief's Journal,* is the first passage in which the author's identification is with the "female figure." Jean Genet is both male and female. Young, poor, a criminal and a beggar, he was also initially the despised drag queen, the *maricone* (faggot), contemptible because he was the female partner in homosexual acts. Older, distinguished by fame, wealthy and secure, he became a male; though never ascending to the full elevation of the pimp (or supermale).

Sexual role is not a matter of biological identity but of class or caste in the hierocratic homosexual society projected in Genet's novels. Because of the perfection with which they ape and exaggerate the "masculine" and "feminine" of heterosexual society, his homosexual characters represent the best contemporary insight into its constitution and beliefs. Granted that their caricature is grotesque, and Genet himself is fully aware of the morbidity of this pastiche, his homosexuals nonetheless have unerringly penetrated to the essence of what heterosexual society imagines to be the character of "masculine" and "feminine," and which it mistakes for the nature of male and female, thereby preserving the traditional relation of the sexes. Sartre's brilliant psychoanalytic biography of Genet describes the sexual life of the pimps and queens, male and female figures, in terms that bear out these distinctions of character and prestige:

This is murder: submissive to a corpse, neglected, unnoticed, gazed at unmindfully and manipulated from behind, the girl queen is metamorphosed into a contemptible female object. She does not even have for the pimp the importance that the sadist attributes to his victim. The latter, though tortured and humiliated, at least remains the focal point of her tormentor's concern. It is indeed she whom he wishes to reach, in her particularity, in the depths of her consciousness. But the fairy is only a receptacle, a vase, a spittoon, which one uses and thinks no more of and which one discards by the very use one makes of it. The pimp masturbates in her. At the very instant when an irresistible force knocks her down, turns her over and punctures her, a dizzying word swoops down upon her, a power hammer that strikes her as if she were a medal: *"Enculé!"* [Faggot]

This is mainly a description of what it is to be female as reflected in the mirror society of homosexuality. But the passage also implies what it is to be male. It is to be mas-

ter, hero, brute, and pimp. Which is also to be irreme-
diably stupid and cowardly. In this feudal relationship of
male and female, pimp and queen, one might expect exchange of servitude for protection. But the typical pimp
never protects his slave, and allows him/her to be beaten,
betrayed, or even killed, responding only with ambiguous
amusement. One is naturally curious to discover just what
the queen does receive in return. The answer appears to
be an intensity of humiliation which constitutes identity
for those who despise themselves. This, in turn, leads us
to the reasons for such self-despair.

W ITH GENET they are quite explicit, and Sartre has
little difficulty outlining them. A bastard, Genet was re-
pudiated at birth and left at an orphanage; the double
rejection of what can only be described as an error from
inception. Adopted then by a family of narrow Morvan
peasants, he was found stealing and sent to grow up in a
children's prison. There he experiences his final ostracism
in being subjected to rape by older and stronger males. He
has now achieved the lowest status in the world as he saw
it; a perfection of opprobrium in being criminal, queer,
and female. It remained only to study and refine his role,
thus the wallowing in self-hatred which both Sartre and
Genet describe as the "femininity" of the passive homosexual. He is feminine because ravished and subjugated by
the male; therefore he must study the slavish gestures of
"femininity" that he may better exalt his master. As a
criminal he is obliged to controvert every decency of the
property-owning class not only through a life of larceny
(material) but through one of betrayal (moral) as well.
And as an outcast, his life's demeanor must be plotted
both to imitate and to contradict every notion of the world
beyond whose boundaries he lives in exile.

But having gone this far, having plunged this low,
Genet studies the values of those who live above him so
that he may further desecrate them. In doing so he acquires the pride of the utterly abject, a condition which
turns out to be next-door to saintliness. As a young beggar
and whore in the Barrio Chino of Barcelona, Genet attained this sanctity and the unshakable self-respect of one

who has truly nothing more to lose. Out of this sprang a wily urge to live. And for those who continue in downright ignominy, the will to live may very plausibly become the will to triumph. This whole cast of thought is generously supported by the French tradition wherein martyrdom is still the highest boon open to the religious imagination. In Catholic Europe sainthood remains, even among the renegades, the loftiest state of grace. That is why Divine, the hero/heroine of *Our Lady of the Flowers*, who is also Genet, is uncontestably a larger spirit than Darling, Gorgui, Armand, Stilitano, and all the other pimps. Not only has she greater courage, humor, imagination, and sensibility than the male oppressors before whom she prostrates herself; she alone has a soul. She has suffered, while they have not, because the consciousness required for suffering is inaccessible to them. And in Divine's mortification, both in the flesh and in the spirit, lies the victory of the saint.

Thus Genet's two great novels, *Our Lady of the Flowers* and *The Thief's Journal*, are tales of an odium converted to grandeur. But together with the rest of his prose fiction they also constitute a painstaking exegesis of the barbarian vassalage of the sexual orders, the power structure of "masculine" and "feminine" as revealed by a homosexual, criminal world that mimics with brutal frankness the bourgeois heterosexual society.

In this way the explication of the homosexual code becomes a satire on the heterosexual one. By virtue of their earnestness, Genet's community of pimps and fairies call into ridicule the behavior they so fervently imitate:

As for slang Divine did not use it, any more than did her cronies, the other Nellys . . .

Slang was for men. It was the male tongue. Like the language of men among the Caribees, it became a secondary sexual attribute. It was like the colored plumage of male birds, like the multi-colored silk garments which are the prerogatives of the warriors of the tribe. It was a crest and spurs. Everyone could understand it, but the only ones who could speak it were the men who at birth received as a gift the gestures, the carriage of the hips, legs and arms, the eyes, the chest, with which one can speak it. One day at one of our bars, when

Mimosa ventured the following words in the course of a sentence ". . . his screwy stories . . . ," the men frowned. Someone said with a threat in his voice: "Broad acting tough."

The virility of the pimp is a transparent egotism posing as strength. His "masculinity" is in fact the most specious of petty self-inflations and is systematically undermined by the true heroes of these adventures, the queens. Though Genet is a great romantic and has created in Divine what is perhaps the last and possibly the most illustrious of those archetypal great-hearted whores so dear to the French tradition, Genet is just as certainly a cold-blooded rationalist whose formidable analytic mind has fastened upon the most fundamental of society's arbitrary follies, its view of sex as a caste structure ratified by nature.

BEGINNING WITH the dissection of sexual attitudes in his prose fiction, Genet has gone on in his plays to survey the parent world of the parasitic homosexual community— that larger society where most of us imagine we are at home. Emerging from the little world of homosexual crime which still concerned him in Deathwatch and The Maids, he brought the truths he had learned there to bear on the complacencies of the "normal" world which for so long had banished and condemned him. His most scathing critique of sexual politics is found in his most recent works for the theater, The Blacks, The Balcony, and The Screens.

What he has to tell this snug and pious enclave will hardly furnish it with the reassuring bromides they have begun to feel the need of and take as a balm from old retainers like Norman Mailer and Henry Miller. Genet submits the entire social code of "masculine" and "feminine" to a disinterested scrutiny and concludes that it is odious.

If Armand is but a brute and a fool, there is really, as Genet demonstrates, no cause for surprise. He was schooled to be such through every element in his education and was clearly given to understand that these traits were no less than the fulfillment of his very nature as a male. All he has learned has taught him to identify "masculine" with force, cruelty, indifference, egotism, and property. It is no wonder that he regards his penis as a talisman: both an instrument to oppress and the very symbol, in fact the reality, of his status: "My cock," he once said, "is worth its weight in gold . . ." At other times he boasts that he can lift a heavy man on the end of it. Armand automatically associates sexuality with power, with his solitary pleasure, and with the pain and humiliation of his partner, who is nothing but an object to him in the most literal sense. Intercourse is an assertion of mastery, one that announces his own higher caste and proves it upon a victim who is expected to surrender, serve, and be satisfied.

Armand, for all his turpitude, is at once both more primitive and more logical than a "gentleman," more honest and direct than the respectable bourgeois whose real convictions he has simply put into practice, and who, by no accident, enjoys reading such passages for the vicarious illusion of mastery which he fancies is offered therein.

The Balcony is Genet's theory of revolution and counterrevolution. The play is set in a brothel and concerns a revolution which ends in failure, preempted by the patrons and staff of the Balcony who assume the roles of the former government. Having studied human relationships in the world of pimp and faggot, Genet has come to understand how sexual caste supersedes all other forms of inegalitarianism: racial, political, or economic. *The Balcony* demonstrates the futility of all forms of revolution which preserve intact the basic unit of exploitation and oppression, that between the sexes, male and female, *or* any of the substitutes for them. Taking the fundamental human connection, that of sexuality, to be the nuclear model of all the more elaborate social constructs growing out of it, Genet perceives that it is in itself not only hopelessly tainted but the very prototype of institutionalized inequality. He is convinced that by dividing humanity into two groups and appointing one to rule over the other by virtue of birthright, the social order has already established and ratified a system of oppression which will underlie and corrupt all other human relationships as well as every area of thought and experience.

The first scene, which takes place between a prostitute and a bishop, epitomizes the play much as it does the society it describes. The cleric holds power only through the myth of religion, itself dependent on the fallacy of sin, in turn conditional on the lie that the female is sexuality itself and therefore an evil worthy of the bishop's condign punishment. By such devious routes does power circle round and round the hopeless mess we have made of sexuality. And money: for it is with money that the woman is purchased, and economic dependency is but another sign of her bondage to a system whose coercive agents are not only mythical but actual. Delusions about sex foster delusions of power, and both depend on the reification of woman.

That the Bishop is actually a gasman visiting the bordello's "chambers of illusions" so that he can vicariously share in the power of the church only clarifies this satire on the sexual class system. Those males relegated to reading gas meters may still participate in the joys of mastery through the one human being any male can buy—a female as whore. And the whore, one wonders, what profits her? Nothing. Her "role" in the ritual theater where sexual, political, and social institutions are so felicitously combined is merely to accommodate the ruling passion of each of her rentiers.

In the second scene, the whore is a thief and a criminal (versions of Genet himself) so that a bank clerk may play at justice and morality. Her judge may order her whipped by a muscular executioner or grant her mercy in a transcendent imitation of the powers-that-be, powers reserved to other more fortunate males. The General of Scene III, following his own notions of masculine majesty, converts his whore into his mount and plays at hero while her mouth bleeds from the bit. No matter with which of the three leading roles of sinner, malefactor, or animal the male client may choose to mime his delusions of grandeur, the presence of the woman is utterly essential. To each masquerading male the female is a mirror in which he beholds himself. And the penultimate moment in his illusory but purchasable power fantasy is the moment when whether as Bishop, Judge, or General, he "fucks" her as woman, as subject, as chattel.

THE POLITICAL WISDOM implicit in Genet's statement in the play is that unless the ideology of real or fantasized virility is abandoned, unless the clinging to male supremacy as a birthright is finally foregone, all systems of oppression will continue to function simply by virtue of their logical and emotional mandate in the primary human situation. But what of the madame herself? Irma, the Balcony's able and dedicated administrator, makes money by selling other women, wherein it may be observed how no institution holds sway without collaborators and overseers. Chosen as queen under the counterrevolution Irma does nothing at all, for queens do not rule. In fact, they do not even exist in themselves; they die as persons once they assume their function, as the Envoy graciously explains. Their function is to serve as figureheads and abstractions to males, just as Chantal, a talented former whore who moves for a moment toward human realization by means of her hope in the revolution, wavers and then is sold anew and converted into the sexual figurehead for the uprising when it becomes corrupt and betrays its radical ideals under the usual excuse of expediency. "In order to win" it adopts the demented consciousness of its opponent and establishes a rotten new version of all it had once stood against. In no time it turns the rebellion into a suicidal carnival, an orgy of blood connected to the old phallic fantasy of "shoot and screw." Its totem is the ritual scapegoat provided by every army's beauty queen since Troy. Once Chantal enters upon the mythical territory of a primitive standard and prize over whom males will tear each other apart, the revolution passes irrevocably into counterrevolution.

Throughout *The Balcony* Genet explores the pathology of virility, the chimera of sexual congress as a paradigm of power over other human beings. He appears to be the only living male writer of first-class literary gifts to have transcended the sexual myths of our era. His critique of the heterosexual politic points the way toward a true sexual revolution, a path which must be explored if any radical social change is to come about. In Genet's analysis, it is fundamentally impossible to change society without changing personality, and sexual personality as it has generally existed must undergo the most drastic overhaul.

If we are to be free at last, Genet proposes in the last scenes of the play, we must first break those chains of our own making through our blind acceptance of common ideas. The three great cages in which we are immured must be dismantled. The first is the potential power of the "Great Figures"—the cleric, the judge and the warrior—elements of myth which have enslaved consciousness in a coil of self-imposed absurdity. The second is the omnipotence of the police state, the only virtual power in a corrupt society, all other forms of coercion being largely psychological. Last, and most insidious of all, is the cage of sex, the cage in which all others are enclosed: for is not the totem of Police Chief George a six-foot, rubber phallus, a "prick of great stature"? And the old myth of sin and virtue, the myth of guilt and innocence, the myth of heroism and cowardice on which the Great Figures repose, old pillars of an old and decadent structure, are also built on the sexual fallacy. (Or as one is tempted to pun, phallacy.) By attempting to replace this corrupt and tottering edifice while preserving its foundations, the revolution's own bid for social transformation inevitably fails and turns into the counterrevolution where the Grand Balcony, a first-class whorehouse, furnishes both costumes and actors for the new pseudo-government.

Genet's play ends as it had begun. Irma turning out the lights informs us we may go home, where all is falser than the theater's rites. The brothel will open again tomorrow for an identical ritual. The sounds of revolution begin again offstage, but unless the Police Chief is permanently imprisoned in his tomb and unless the new rebels have truly forsworn the customary idiocy of the old sexual politics, there will be no revolution. Sex is deep at the heart of our troubles, Genet is urging, and unless we eliminate the most pernicious of our systems of oppression, unless we go to the very center of the sexual politic and its sick delirium of power and violence, all our efforts at liberation will only land us again in the same primordial stews.

The Fear of Flying

Mona Van Duyn

*". . . shall it be given us to speak in the spiritual, un-
earthly voice of a bat or a jet?"*

At the airport, ready to leave on my little trip,
I tell you goodbye and start
to get in line at the door, our relationship
so old we don't kiss, when my heart

goes crazy with pain and fear, jumps in my throat,
my stomach heaves, I want
to get out of this frozen skin and run for the heat
of your body and yet I can't.

Every time I'm about to get on a plane it's the same
sick terror. I've got to know what
brings on such hysteria, what in God's name
is the matter with me. It's not

the fear of death. You've rehearsed me so often in that,
with your false springs, your icy
changes of heart and face, I'm bored at the thought
of there being no more me

to see and feel them. It's not as if we were young
and couldn't bear to part—
far from it. We've been yoked together so long
it doesn't even hurt

that we both forget every anniversary.
There were good years together,
one has to remember that towards the end, surely—
moondazzle, peach weather,

brilliant noons, eloquent storms, sweet
new spears of tenderness,

all the lovely things, natural and trite,
one has to believe, I guess,

make life worth living, made it worth our while
to have come to middle age
with such brutal knowledge of one another. How well
I know each clever image

you present in public, the four parts you play
(none of them now for me):
The cool, brittle disillusioned roué,
handsome as a fall tree,

with secret softnesses beneath, to be found
and nursed into late bloom,
much rarer of course than of April's callow ground,
by someone in the room.

Or, your hair redyed, the hand-holder,
fresh buds in your buttonhole,
the whole green youth bit again, the breezy,
twittery, dancing, boy-girl

approach. (How you pull that bright illusion out
of the hat at your age
over and over, I'll never know. It's what,
watching it from offstage,

can hurt me most, whose one-and-only springtime
in one of yours is over.)
Or, with faintly snow-streaked hair, you mime
the quiet, fatherly lover,

all passion spent, not at all dangerous—
yes, that appeals to some.
How often you used to fool me with that face
of pure, restful welcome—

then, if I leaned against you, I'd feel the sleet
of your look, go numb at your blast
of contempt, turn to a snow-wife of hate.
And we know, don't we, the last

of your roles? Remember, my dear, I played it with you
for long, bountiful seasons?
We bathed, we melted down to the bone in the blue
air, the ripe suns

of ourselves, stretched and vined together all over,
it seemed, sweltered, grew

lush undergrowth, weeds, flowers, groundcover.
I played and played with you,

day after burning day, the part of our lives
truest, perhaps, best,
and still can play it briefly if someone believes
I can: the sensualist.

Your cheek used to cool first and then rewarm,
but now our hot coinciding
is rare. Is this wordy drizzle a late-summer storm
or an autumnal? I'm hiding

something that wants to scream out, "Wait! Not yet!
It's too soon for me
to go away into thin air," a thing that
I can't say or see.

I see it, foolish and clear, and say it. Sometimes,
our minds are so used to whirling,
it's hard to believe the simple meters and rhymes
and explanations. Darling,

my world, my senses' home, familiar monster,
it would seem that I still love you,
and, like a schoolgirl deep in her first despair,
I hate to go above you.

Like. . .

Rosalyn Drexler

I

ABOUT A YEAR AGO I was depressed. And I didn't have any place to go. But you know, there's always someplace to go in New York. Like the NBC tours, the UN, or the movies. It was mid-afternoon. The afternoon is for very unhip places. But I was really so depressed that I thought I'd hide out in the movies.

The picture didn't help . . . a huge mutilated corpse, in technicolor, lay bleeding into an oriental rug. His missing parts were being enumerated by a detective, almost seductively, to a younger member of the police force: ". . . penis cut off . . ."

I brought a noncarbonated drink to my seat just as the detective examined some sand on the floor of the dead bachelor's digs. His eyes seemed foamy and pale yellow as he rose, but adjusted to piercing blue as he said:

"Hummmmmmmnnnn, sand . . ."

Later on in the movie, just when the guy who supposedly did it (also a homosexual) was jerking against his leather accessories in the "hot" seat, I thought I felt a feel at my thigh. It was hard to tell. I looked down. All I could see was the thick edge of a herringbone tweed overcoat jammed between the seats. The guy next to me looked down too, as if he was helping me. We both shrugged and went back to the death chamber. But we weren't there long.

Then I felt it again. Sort of like warm butterflies brushing by, landing and taking off of my thigh. I let my own hand suddenly drop loose at my side, and I caught him! I grabbed his hand and squeezed as hard as I could. His bones rose toward the middle of my relentless palm like a log jam.

36

"Ouch!" he said. "Ouch!" He tried to withdraw his hand. I gave him a terrific whack on the wrist.

"Ouch!"

"You asked for it."

"Lay off, damn it!"

I poured the remaining drops of my sickly sweet drink into the lap of (I found out later) Paul Partch. I grinned into his face. But I don't think he saw it.

"See you later," I threatened. ". . . outside!" He whispered, "Okay." And left his seat. I stayed to see the end of the film before I went out to wait for the creep.

II

OKAY," I whispered, glad to get away. I hadn't bargained for that. Usually they just change their seats. I went down to the men's room, hurrying along and pushing a copy of *Newsweek* into my already stuffed coat pocket. I had about three dirty handkerchiefs, theater tickets, crushed art announcements, crumbs, and pencils in there already. On the pot I took out the rolled-up *Newsweek* to swat roaches with. It was hot in there; the roaches crawled down the pipes and across the tiles. Some were hard to see. But I forced myself to see them because I didn't want to think about anything else. The albinos looked like mobilized sesame seeds; I imagined that some of them would be able, though half dead, to crawl into my white socks and arrive home with me to breed in my own unsanitary bathroom. The brown ones trembled on legs thin as coat thread and made their escape by stitching their way under the door. One of them stuck to the sole of my new loafers. I wiped tiny segments of the crushed brown pastry shell from my shoe. I stared at the damp spot on the sole of my shoe, and had thoughts.

Small things fill me with horror: puffballs splitting open in the wind. Crawling creatures squirming free. My tiny mother. When I was five years old I hid under the bed crying my heart out: "I don't want a small mommy." Her diminutive grace had been threatening to me. She seemed like a toy, capable of being broken and thrown away. By me? When I was a fourteen-year-old giant I hit my mother for frying my eggs the wrong way. She fell down. Lay at my feet like a cloth effigy: faceless, boneless, but resembling herself.

I stared at the damp spot on the sole of my shoe and thought about my taste in women. As I so often ask myself, "Dear God, why do I get hot for big?" The very question gets me hot. To be overcome by big! To be handled roughly by the last in line, the funky fat, the tough tomboy!

These moments have been few and far between: as far between as a jump from rim to rim across the Grand Canyon. I used to think about it a lot—how to antagonize the plug-uglies so that they would have it in for me and attack!

I knew that aggressive girl was waiting for me outside. My hand still tingled from its thrilling encounter; I thought, "What kind of thigh is it she has? Is it firm and muscular? Tawny and terrible?" The situation had great utility for me. But still I stayed in the john, tempting fate to take her away, pretending I was in no hurry. My hangup is waiting; waiting for opportunity to pass me by. My unhappiness is a relief—it keeps my nose buried in books, my eyes glued to paintings and sculpture, and my hand . . . All solitary pleasures.

I tried to get off the pot. It might have been a glue pot the way I stuck to it. I spoke to myself sternly: "Get off the pot!" Didn't pay any attention. I then rolled two small pieces of paper into nose plugs and gently inserted them, continued speaking to myself: "The smoke of the dragon is frozen. The dragon is trapped in calcimine cavern where he anticipates with relish the advent of a fresh maiden." I knew it wasn't so. One foot had fallen asleep. My rear was numb. Still I couldn't make my move; "up, up, *and away!*" Other men had come and gone, pissed and flushed into the porcelain row of orange squeezer urinals, sat in the cabinet next to mine and finished in good style. But there I was. I who had most to gain. There I was fouling the air with fear, peristalting farts into the sealed bowl. I produced a pleasing quickie fantasy using the unknown girl whom I had hoped would be mad enough to want to even the score with me outside.

She takes me to her room. On the way she shoves me into the shadowy depths of Davega's sporting goods store and tells me her name while forcing me to my knees with a full nelson. I am unable to break her grip. She presses down on the back of my neck with locked fingers. Her arms fit under mine comfortably, like a life jacket. I feel her weight floating on my back, both of us sinking to the depths. I suffer rapture of the deep. Then she rescues me, saying, "I'm sorry, I didn't mean to hurt you." And I say, "You won't hurt me. You're strong but gentle." "Oh yeah," she says, "Try this on for size." And she embraces me. She hugs me, saying, "This is the bear hug for which I am famous. Only the bear is better than I am." I gasp for mercy, both lungs deflating and ribs caving in. "Okay," she says, "mercy for the time being. Where do you live?" We proceed, as if nothing had happened, to my place, where the minute we get inside the door she takes me down, retains her advantage with an armlock, grapevines both legs, pins me to the dusty planks of the hall floor, and says, "Say uncle!" I shout, "Uncle! I'd do anything for you, you Glamazon!" And she says, "Anything? Well then, suck my pussy." And I have to do it because she's the champ, the winner, the goddess . . . the diva who makes me dive.

Someone knocked on the door. "Anyone in there?"

"Be right out," I blurted, maneuvering a hardon. I pulled up my clean new jockey shorts and noticed an exclamation point of brown dividing the clean side from the clean side. "Hard-edge expressionism," I thought. "At last an art reeking of refusal, and redolent of decay, for rich and poor alike." My hardon had disappeared. I flipped the latch and came out.

III

OUTSIDE, he put his arm up as though to shield his sensitive eyes from the light and in that way to sneak by her. But she stood her ground, causing him to walk right into her.

"Excuse me, please," he said, still not looking.

"Are you sick or somethin'?" she said.

"I don't believe so."

"You don't know me?"

"Right, I don't know you." His arm was down and he was staring straight into her blue eyes.

"But you touched me!"

"It was an accident and I'm sorry."

"You're a liar."

"Afraid not . . . I don't have to go around putting my hands on women I don't even know, in the dark."

"Your nail tore my nylon."

He quickly glanced toward his ragged fingernails. Why did he neglect them? "Look, it won't do any good discussing this notion of yours in the street. Why don't we go somewhere for a cup of coffee?"

"Okay, a cup of coffee. I'd like to find out what makes . . . What's your name?"

"Paul."

"I'd like to find out what makes Paul tick."

"What's your name?"

"Rosa."

They went to Hector's Cafeteria where they eyed each other suspiciously across a wet table. Rosa's finger, in careful, slippery cursive, wrote R-O-S-A.

"Would you care for something?" Paul asked, watching her cold red finger.

"Think I'll just warm up first. Then I'd like a coffee regular."

"What's regular?" Paul asked, wondering if perhaps she thought regular was something else than what he thought it was.

"With everything."

"Cream, sugar?"

"Yeah! What's the trouble, haven't you ever heard someone ask for regular?"

"Well," Paul said pedantically, "what is regular for one, may be intermittent for another. . . . For instance, I like my coffee black, and it is only on occasion, when somebody makes a mistake, that I take coffee with cream and sugar."

"What else do you do?" Rosa asked. "Besides drinking

bitter coffee and picking girls up in the movies?" She was hoping he was someone with a pad of his own and that he would invite her to stay the night.

Paul chucked her under the chin as if she had said something pleasing to him. "What do I do?"

"Yeah, what?"

"I am interested in many things. Among them art, writing, sports, theater, women."

"You got a studio?"

"No, I don't paint, I write about those who do. I'm a critic." Paul was waiting for an opening in the conversation to ask his most important question.

"Isn't it a drag for you to have to be dependent on what someone else does, for what you do?" Rosa said. "I mean, what if there were no artists? That's a possibility. What if robots took over? What would you do then?" Rosa crossed her arms over her chest, sure she had him now.

Paul noticed her well-shaped arms powerfully locking into one another. Her stern expression turned his knees to jelly and his tongue to paste. "No, no. You got me wrong. I help clarify . . . my writing is the best writing of its kind that you'll read anywhere. I try to write creatively, it's not dry-as-dust stuff, not the kind of school pedantry you imagine. I'll take you home after we have something to eat, and show you. . . . Do you read much?"

"Oh," Rosa said sweetly, "oh, I mostly look at the pictures. It's only intermittently that I read the words. The pictures are regular, the words are black and bitter."

"The pictures are black and bitter these days too," Paul answered, but she didn't take him up on it. She was not prejudiced, understood both sides, especially the black side because she had once slept with a black poet. He had even come to hate her "pink, pink, you stink," face, because she thought their problems were personal and he insisted that they were racial.

"And another thing," Paul said. "Getting back to what you said about my work depending on the work of others— we are all dependent on each other, some more than others. Do you mean to say that you're a complete original?"

"Original what?" Rosa asked. She was willing to be dependent on him for a couple of nights, and that wasn't original. Everybody she knew was dependent that way.

"That you're original in what you do . . . that your thing, whatever that is, has nothing to do with what other people are doing!" He watched her original and unique face take on a petulant and childish expression. Her round flaming cheeks, strong nose, and full licky-lips reminded him of a Russian heroine from the *Snow Maiden*. She was still wearing a big fox-fur hat, which was round too, like her face, and tied under her chin. "Why don't you take that hat off? Aren't you too hot?" He felt tenderness toward her, she was so aggressively stupid.

"Okay. I forgot I had it on." She began laughing. "No wonder I had trouble hearing you. But isn't it groovy! I found it in a movie, and boy does it come in handy!" She put both hands in it, as if it were a muff, then extended it toward Paul. "Feel it. It's so exciting to feel. Those hundreds of hairs tickle like crazy. Just run your hands over the tips—isn't it sexy?"

Paul let the palms of his hands skim over the hat, barely touching. It did feel good. So, she was sensual. That was good too. She might be the winning combination.

"What do you do?" Paul asked. "Where do you come from? Where are you going? Why didn't you change your seat in the movies the way other women do after I touch them?"

"What, me run from you? Hah! Besides, I was in a murderous mood. I would have challenged King Kong if he bothered me. And to answer your other questions, I don't do anything, but someday I will. I just know I have all this talent stored up inside. I want to keep going, see everything, do everything. I'm not ready to get hung on some narrow, no-view occupation. I mean, maybe I will design some posters for a group I know, or talk a book into a tape. I already have the title: *Rosa, So Far*. I'd like to do that. Sometimes I write a poem when I feel bad, like when my old man left me and went to San Francisco. Know anybody driving there, an artist or something?"

"Sorry. Don't you have a family?"

"Why?" Rosa asked, growing suspicious. "Should I have?"

"I wondered how old you are, that's all."

"I'm old enough to be on my own. I've been on my own since I was fifteen. Say, you aren't a detective, are you? Strike that out. If you are, you have a pretty perverse way of picking up suspects. Do you do that often, feel women up in the movies?"

"I was attracted to you," Paul said.

"In the dark?"

"Electrical vibrations. You drew me to you." It was true.

"Know what? I have a lot of electricity in me. When I wear boots and walk across a rug I can't even open a door without getting a shock. I can't even kiss or hold a subway token, it hurts."

"Don't wear boots," Paul offered, trying to be funny.

"That's all I have is these old things." Rosa held one foot out for him to see. "They used to be beautiful, but you can't keep suede clean. They used to be the color of . . . oh they used to be a light tan. Tantalizing tan. Now you can see everything I've gone through stain by stain. Grease, blood, rain, snow. Snow leaves a white ridge at the toe. I didn't know that snow actually had the color white in it."

"Would you like that coffee now?" Paul asked.

"I don't like coffee," Rosa said. "It's just what I order when I don't want to eat or drink. I watch it get cold and then I leave it."

"You have a beautiful face," Paul said.

"That's cool." Rosa was pleased. "How would you review my face? Give me an example of your style."

"I can't talk my style, I have to write it."

"Oh try! I want to hear about my face, it's the nicest thing about me."

"If I tell you about your face, will you tell me about you? Just a few things so that I can begin to know you better. You're a very unusual girl. I like you a lot."

Rosa gave Paul a small Japanese sketch pad which she took out of a straw bag she was carrying. "Here, you can use it too, I carry it in case I think something memorable. You know how the things you really feel and want to say can get away from you . . . even one word on a page, like *broiled 2/2/68.*"

"What do you mean by broiled?" Paul asked.

"Like it was a cold day and I wrote *broiled* to remind me of the sun, and I also had a quarter of a broiled chicken at a friend's house on 2/2/68, and my mom gave me a crisp new bill . . . and well it was a broiled day . . . Doesn't that Japanese paper make writing look artistic? Turn past the scribbles, there's a clean page somewhere in the middle. No, not there, that's where I used red ink to write about the war, you know to look like blood, but it went through and stained almost all the other pages. . . . Yeah, but then I thought that's the way it is . . . everybody's got blood on them . . . everybody's in the book."

Paul was moved by the simple child-woman making poetry out of horror. The scribbles he had flipped past resembled Art Brut: one huge eye with repeated outlines rippled across an entire page, on another page a nude figure crouched with her head in her hands, long strands of hair undulating about her like rope. "She's either talented or sick, maybe both," Paul thought. Again he felt a rush of tenderness toward her . . . her brusque offering of the book and her vulnerability.

"Are you sure you want me to write in this? It's such a private book," he asked.

"Yeah, go ahead. What you write is part of what happened to me today. It doesn't have to be good. I mean it can be good if it is. Don't be a drag, accept!" She lit a Turkish cigarette. "I love these, they're packed real tight and last a long time and they're sweet. When I have the bread I get the best. I'm an aristocrat but I'm temporarily wiped out." She laughed at herself and settled back to watch Paul write. He wrote:

ROSA ROSA (Hector's Cafeteria Gallery) In this her first show, begins her career as a very personal face with a genuinely poetic vision. Filled with sentiment, she makes the face express her feelings. Her eyes bathe in the limpid expanse of wide-eyed ultramarine incredulity. Knowledgeable and controlled, she projects a nose that remains substantial. Her mouth tries for mobility in the Baroque sense, curling fluidly over her teeth. The contour of her face, best evoked by jawbone and cheekbone, extend the formal requirements of structure. Within her particular dimensions she enmeshes her viewer in a network of barely perceptible vein-traps pulsing beneath a heavy impasto of Winsor-Newton flesh tint. Straightforward, yet displaying an inherent gentility if not gentleness, the reality of this face attains some of the quality of a dream. This may be due to the interior of Hector's Cafeteria, which is used as a neutral ground but insists on being just corny. This is a Rosa to watch. She shows promise.

Paul shut the book and handed it to Rosa.

"Why'd you close it?" she asked. "I'm going to read it anyway."

"Not here," Paul said.

"I'm too curious to wait. I want to read about me, me, me."

She found the page and eagerly scanned the tight scrawl to the end. "Wow!"

"Wow what?" Paul asked.

"Wow, I don't understand it. But it sounds very smart."

"I wrote it as if I was reviewing your face in an art magazine."

"Oh. I never read one of those. But I'll tell you this, if I ever read what you wrote about my face, I wouldn't be able to recognize it."

"I warned you. I gave you a chance to take back your book." Paul was disappointed. Perhaps he had invested her with too much native intelligence.

"Hey," Rosa said kindly, "it's cool . . . it's you . . . dig yourself! You probably wouldn't like what I like either. Are you famous? You might be for all I know."

That was really rubbing it in. Oh, he had a few admirers, readers who wrote letters to the editor praising P.P. (Paul Partch) for a brilliant analysis or a well-turned phrase, but that wasn't often. Occasionally some obscure artist would gift him with a small work, but Dubuffet, Lichtenstein, Warhol, Oldenburg, Wesselman, Hinman, hung on other walls. More popular colleagues—the party-goers, art-history majors, homosexuals—received the lion's share, the expensive cuts. Paul had been straining to coin a new word for the new art, a word as strong as "Pop," "Op," or "Minimal." A few times he had inserted the phrase

"Stop Art," to express his feeling that art was coming to an end (it had no place to go), but the locution was not picked up. Nobody wanted to stop anything. Everybody wanted to start something. To be the first, not the last.

"Do you mind if I have my coffee now?" Paul asked. "And if you want anything, tell me and I'll be glad to get it. Aren't you hungry?"

"Naw, I'm not. My stomach's shrunk. I don't eat very much."

"Stomach shrunk?" Paul wondered how such an obviously healthy girl could have a shrunken stomach.

"I went on a strict diet, you know, no bread to buy bread. Besides, men don't like fat women."

"Shows how much you know," Paul said. "A big strapping girl full of vitality is extremely attractive to a man. . . . to me at least."

"Well you're out of it," Rosa said. "The eating thing has become too important, you know—feed the body, starve the mind."

Paul brought back a cup of black coffee and a piece of cherry cheese cake.

"Is that ever disgusting," Rosa said. "Did you know that cheese cake doesn't have any cheese in it, and the cherries are poisonous? The red dye in them can cause nephritis in small children if they eat too many of them. Don't eat it. Ugh! I hate artificial stuff!"

Paul felt it incumbent on him to make a great show of eating and enjoying the cake. Rosa watched in amazement as he gobbled it down.

"What a pig! My mother used to be a pig till she got cancer. Now she can't hardly suck ice-water out of a soaked sponge."

Startled by this sudden unpleasant information, Paul said, "That's awful. Do you live with your mother?"

"Are you gullible!" she said, laughing. "I made that story up. My real true life story is so boring that I wouldn't bother boring you with it. I have a mother and a father and they're healthy and fat and old and stupid and too much! I love them so much because they're so much fun to bug. I hope I never see them again. Why don't we leave now? There's too many people in one place breathing the air up. Have you ever thought about how what you breathe comes out of thousands of nostrils and lungs, some of them diseased?"

"Do you suggest we stop breathing?"

"I have an idea. I got it from an article on Japan. You know the air in Tokyo is worse than the air in New York— well they have oxygen-vending machines in the street for people who want a breath of fresh air. It would be cheaper than taking a trip to the country if they had that in New York. What if you could buy a small oxygen bomb with a nozzle to put over your nose? It would sell like crazy and everyone would get high."

Smiling, she reached out and held one of his hands between her two, pressing gently, enjoying her idea. She had a habit of touching, caressing another person when she was particularly pleased with herself.

"You have a lot of weird ideas," Paul said. He wondered what her reaction would be when he sprung his weird ideas on her.

"Yeah, I'm pretty wild. Everyone says that. Almost everything I do or say is ahead of my time. My mind's going a mile a minute. . . . I say or do whatever I think of . . . don't know what makes me that way. I just like to be first. But don't think I lack soul!"

"Soul?" Paul would rather have heard about her body.

"Sure. I believe in soul. A soul is the spiritual thing that allows me to cop out of a bad situation but at the same time to dig the person I leave, and to dig myself more."

What she was trying to tell him was that if they got together and she left him suddenly, it wouldn't be because she hated him, it would be because she wanted to make another scene. She was not a bitch . . . just restless.

"A person like you is what I call irresponsible," Paul said.

Rosa turned his coffee cup upside down and rested her elbow on it. She had to do something to relieve the tense feeling he was giving her. Not that she didn't intend sharing his bed with him that evening, but fucking would have to be easier than this conversation.

"How come a nice girl like you was alone in the movies? What brought you in?" He removed the cup from under her elbow and playfully took her hand, maneuvering their arms into position for an arm wrestle. Maybe he wouldn't have to ask the important question.

"I came in out of the cold," Rosa replied, then added, "My horoscope for today was interesting, it indicated I would meet you. It said, 'Don't worry about the orthodox; push ahead; stars which come into play just after mid-month will tend to focus your attention on a new eccentric acquaintance. Your affairs and activities could very easily take on a hint of mystery or secrecy indoors, although a number of other people will be present.' There it is . . . you and me in the movies. What's your sign?"

"Crossed purposes," Paul answered, as he tried to bring her arm down to the table. She was a better arm-wrestler than he had expected. He let her play at the top of her strength for a while before exerting all of his power and winning. But it was hard. "Not bad for a girl," he said, knowing that she was extraordinary, and he was hot. "With a little experience you could beat me."

"How'd I get into that?" Rosa asked, staring at him. "I never did that before."

"Lots of things you never did before," he said confidently. "Shall we go?"

Outside, Paul told Rosa to call a cab. "Go on, I can afford it. There's one about two blocks up."

"Why don't you?" Rosa asked.

"You just seem so capable," Paul said, "and I wanted to see you run."

"I'm not about to run up and down the street waving at cabs. That's what men are supposed to do."

"If I were a cab driver, I'd rather stop for you than for me," Paul said.

"If you don't stop being such a head fucker I'm gonna walk in the other direction."

"What other direction?"

"Opposite from where you want to go with me."

A cab with an off-duty light stopped in front of the cafeteria. Paul argued the driver into taking them to West 49th Street, between Ninth and Tenth, where he lived.

"We could have walked," Rosa said. "It's only a few blocks."

IV

Paul took a long time opening the door to his flat. He couldn't seem to find the right key.

"Whatdya need all those keys for?" I asked. "You got more than one place?" Yet I liked the sound and look of his bunch of keys. Very mysterious music for opening a lock. I groove on sound effects; what a fabulous way to furnish an apartment, with sound effects and film projections: like snow and the sound of softly falling snow filling the entire room. How great it would be in the summertime for instance: air-conditioning, snow falling, a transparent pocket of winter . . . outside, the sun burning holes in everybody's paper clothing.

"I've had these keys for years," Paul said to me, still fumbling and fingering them. "Don't know what half of them are for anymore."

"Well why don't you put a piece of colored masking tape on the ones you do use, so you don't have to stand around in the cold hall every time you come home." I have a practical side too.

As we walked down the long dark hall of his flat, a string from the light brushed my face. "Here's the light," I said, and pulled the string. "Not very bright, is it!" Sixty watts of illumination from the one bare bulb was just enough for me to see three doors to the right, a dirty wall to the left, and straight ahead one large room with no doors. I don't like doors anyway. I like to open things up, knock down walls, make holes in the floor to the apartment below. Once my friend had a place right below mine and we made a hole in the living room floor and used a ladder to climb up and down. The landlord kicked us out, but then he raised the rent, put in real stairs, and rented the apartment as a duplex. It takes daring to carry through an original idea. "How many rooms do you have?" I asked Paul.

"Kitchen, bathroom, bedroom, and a living room. Follow me."

We threw our coats on a broken-down brown couch in the living room. I reached into my ample, brightly colored

Mexican straw bag and took out my Turkish cigarettes.

"Do you have to smoke?" Paul asked.

"Why, don't you?"

"No," Paul answered, "and I can't stand the taste of it on someone's breath."

"Great beginning," I said. "What do I do about that?"

"Stop smoking."

"Just like that?"

"Yeah, just like that."

I wasn't about to listen to him. I mean it wasn't a habit with me, I didn't have to smoke. I just really loved to smoke. The whole ritual, asking for my brand to taking the first puff, inhaling, and feeling that scratchy ache of pleasure fill my lungs and my head with peace . . .

"You're really uptight," I told Paul, "and you don't know what you're talking about. It's easy to talk about something you don't know about, like the Pope talking about sex." But the cigarette jutting from between my fingers looked like an awkward sixth finger drained of blood, yet festering at the tip. "Got an ashtray?" He brought me a cracked saucer, and I stubbed the cigarette out on it.

"Thanks," Paul said.

"So let's see the rest of your place. You have a phone?"

"It's in the bedroom. Feel free."

I could see his face tighten for a second.

"It's just a local call," I said. "I might not even make it."

"Whatever you say."

The bedroom was a box containing a mattress on springs; I was glad to see the mattress because for the last couple of nights I had slept on the floor of a friend's pad near St. Marks Place. Near the mattress were three cartons of books, a desk, and a chair. Underwear lay about the floor. The sheets were dirty, and a pile of old newspapers near the bed served as a night table. There was a Big Ben alarm clock on the newspapers.

"Don't you have a lamp?" I asked. The glare from the ceiling hurt my eyes, and it wasn't very romantic either. I thought of some tiny red veins on my thighs and the rough skin on the soles of my feet. Hard to be exciting when the light itself dazzles. I'm surprised there aren't any light freaks. One bare light, if stared at long enough, wraps the skull in bandages, seals nirvana behind bone, and blinds the orgasm. "That light in the ceiling could blind you."

"It does," Paul said.

"Why don't you get a lamp, or some kind of shade?"

"I never think of it unless I'm lying here reading."

"You'd better take care of your eyes." I put my straw bag down on the floor. Scratchy bastard of a bag. It marked my arm. Everything I owned was in that bag. My past and future was in that bag. Things were in that bag.

"What's in that bag?" He lifted it a few times, indicating that it was ridiculously heavy.

"Clothes and things. Telephone book, cigarettes, make-up, douche powder, douche, Dexies, Meth, Thorazine, vitamin pills, rose-hip gum, sugar cubes, perfume, jewelry, the *I-Ching*, the *Egyptian Book of the Dead*, Emco Foam . . ."

Emco Foam works a lot better for me than the pill. Anyway I'm afraid of the pill, I read that there is conclusive evidence that it causes blood clots in the lungs. I don't need that. I really recommend Emco Foam, though, because it's easy to use—one plungerful of invisible, odorless foam and the entire cervix is coated and protected from the thousands of lash-tailed sperm that try to enter. Let your vagina be a fortress! But not always. When Paul went into the kitchen to bring me a glass of water, I put the Emco Kit under the pillow. The doctor at the Birth Control Clinic said that I should put it in every night before retiring, before every intercourse, but I don't. What if someone wants to go down on you? Can you imagine the taste? So I wait. See what the inclination is. Act accordingly.

"What this place needs is some color," I thought. "Flowers, curtains, posters . . . and some groovy incense." I dug in my bag and came up with a bottle of Liebe Strawberry cologne in a round black bottle, which I had bought at the White Elephant in the East Village. I stood on the kitchen chair that was in the bedroom and threw some cologne at the light bulb. It hit the hot surface and steamed off, like a weather control experiment. The delicate scent of crushed strawberries filled the room. Inhaling deeply I walked around the room with my eyes closed, chanting: "I love strawberries, I love strawberries, I love strawberries . . ." Sometimes I can get myself into states of ecstasy by repeating sounds, words.

In mid-chant I plumped myself onto the bed. Then I began to feel ridiculous. I said to myself, "What do I mean I love strawberries? I don't know anything about strawberries. I don't know if they grow on a bush or in the ground, in the shade or in the sun, whether they come out of blossoms like apples, or what. Don't you need full knowledge, case history, origin, to love?" Bullshit. Love is love. It creates its own history. From the very first taste I was hooked. "Oh luscious stromberries I love you, stromberries, stromberries, deluscious stromberries . . ." I chanted again.

"Were you on the telephone?" Nervous Paul reared his suspicious head once again. In his hand was a tall glass of ice water.

"Nope, I was talking to myself. Haven't you ever done that?"

"I do it all the time," he said, handing me the glass of water. I leaned the glass against my cheek for a few seconds to bring back the color I had come in with.

"Say Paul, you're well informed aren't you?" He shrugged his shoulders. "What I was wondering about was, what do you know about strawberries?"

"Strawberries?" he said. "That's funny, I smell strawberries. Can the power of suggestion be that strong?" He took swift short sniffs of the air.

I told him that the fragrance in the room had not been suggested to him subliminally, that speaking about things did not make you able to smell them. That the smell did indeed exist. Up there on the light bulb, where I had splashed it.

"What other magic can you do? That was a lovely, thoughtful action to take in this musty, moldy room. Every time I put on the light I'll think of you, at least while the fragrance lasts."

"Go out again," I said, "I want to try something. Wait in the hall." He waited patiently while I took off all my clothes and lay on top of the blanket still as death, one arm dangling off the side of the mattress. I knew I looked beautiful that way—soft, receptive, passively offering up my body. "Come in now," I called. "You can come in now."

V

A STROKE of genius," I thought. "A stroke of genius on her part. How could she have guessed what makes me impotent!" She lay on my bed, dirty feet planted firmly on my sheet, like a giant aphid dropped from the split of a ripe pod. She looked stunned, and the backbone of the bed broken.

"Sleep with me," she asked, pleading. "Sleep with me love." I stood at the door and watched her body be nothing to nobody. "Don't you like girls?" she asked. Then she took another stupid pose, knees up, head back. Hiding everything.

"You know better than that," I answered. "Would I have taken you here for conversation?"

She stared at me, trying to ESP my thoughts, my motives.

"Are you thinking of the number five?" she asked. "Because I just got a vibration of the number five." She bit her lip. That was interesting. It was more interesting than having her just lie there waiting for me to rape her. And the way she was embarrassed and tried to change the subject began to move me too. After all, it was Rosa who was naked and Rosa who was rejected.

"I'm not thinking about any numbers," I said. "Why, are you?"

"I thought it would bring us closer together if I could receive your secret messages."

"Believe me, you haven't a clue!" I said.

"What were you thinking?" she asked. She must have been cold, but she remained on top of the blanket.

"I was thinking you could really turn me on, except . . ."

"Except what?" she asked.

"Except it was a shock seeing you dressed one minute and undressed the next." I was almost shouting.

"What's so shocking about the human body?" she shouted

back at me, rising on the bed. Her head almost touched the ceiling. Rather imposing. She grew bigger than both of us, imperiously commanding the situation. She kept pressing her point, rather poetically, I thought. "The skin is just a waterproof covering, the breasts are warm milk jugs and pacifiers, the hair is for warmth, the insides are a juice factory and baby hotel, the limbs are for traveling, the face is for knowing who you're talking to . . . Wow! Come on, it's just me, a chick on the evolutionary scale. We balance each other out!" She started to reach for a cigarette. I gave her a dirty look. "Don't look at me that way," she said. "So what if I coughed a couple of times in the cab, and maybe this pimple on my shoulder looks like a boil to you, but don't worry I had a complete medical checkup last week including a free chest X-ray. I got a clean bill of health. Don't know how I stay so healthy."

I am a bug about health. Her cough in the cab had bothered me. Her denials made me suspicious. "Why'd you go? What were your symptoms?"

She became more and more defiant, defending herself against me, the nut. "Symptoms? I didn't have any. But you know those signs in the subway: HAVE A CHECKUP NOW . . . FREE CHEST X-RAY . . . YOU MAY HAVE DIABETES . . . SYPHILIS IS A DISEASE NOT A DIRTY WORD! I figured it would be groovy to spend the day getting all those free tests. I stayed up all night so I could get to the clinic on time in the morning. That's the only way I get anywhere in the morning, the morning has to sneak up on me. Once I go to sleep, there is no dawn. No dawn, no executions, right?"

What had she ever witnessed at dawn? Why did she think of dawn and executions, instead of dawn and the birth of a new day? I supposed it was her B-movie mentality. She had nothing to fear. I did. "Move over," I said.

"This far enough?" She made a place for me beside her, as if we were about to share a lunch sitting on a school bench. She pulled the sheet over her breasts, still believing that the sight of her nude body disturbed me. "Don't worry, I won't attack you." She laughed and her tongue leaped like a frog on a lily pad. It was a dirty gesture, like a flick of the imagination. I wanted to feel her tongue strike my cheek, my lips, my nose. I think I blushed as I asked, "Why won't you rape me, Rosa?"

Completely confused, she answered, "This is too stupid for words. What do you want?"

It was impossible to tell her, so instead I said, "I want to hear more about your life." I hoped she wouldn't take me up on it.

"This is my life," she said. "I'm trying to find my twin brother, we were separated at birth when my parents died and left us orphans. Are you my brother? Let's see, I have a birthmark on the inside of my thigh. He did too." She was becoming hysterical and giddy. "Let's see the inside of your thigh!" She began tussling with me out of desperation, trying to get my pants off. Things were going my way. She was very strong and managed to remove my trousers. I became tremendously excited. Rolling and tumbling, she then removed the rest of my clothing. Forcing my thighs apart she continued playing her game. "You're not my brother. You're an imposter! You lack the birthmark."

My humor returned with my birthright, a healthy erection. "This is my birthmark, I have this," I said, feeling grateful to her for having invented such a charming game. She stood on the bed and pulled the light string, dragging the dark down over us. I held her close. She smelled clean and alive, a little like smoked ham . . . probably from the cigarettes. My instincts about her had been correct, she was strong and could hold her own. I had the evidence of the arm wrestle and the bed wrestle. I gave her back her native intelligence. She must have planned my seduction in just this way, advancing, retreating, advancing, retreating, till I was in a frenzy. Women have the whole world in their hand, not God. And they can squeeze or carry you gently at will, and they know it. Her weight on top of me made me feel so safe, so secure, like a little marine beast being carried along in the murky folds of a mammoth sea creature. Her pearly flesh sprung two pink nipples, sprawling across her chest like sea anemones; I suckled, hanging on as she plummeted downward to the very bottom of the sea: the sea was salt . . . I could taste it . . . and cool . . . I could feel it . . . and merciless as it crashed down on us, pressing Rosa into me. I couldn't help it. I came too fast. It was good. I didn't even feel guilty. The lovely girl slid off me without a sound. But after a few minutes of blotting her belly with the sheet, she said pleasantly, "It's never good the first time you meet someone. I really like you very much. We gotta get used to each other. You're different."

We fell asleep back to back in my bed.

VI

I slept," I said to Paul. It amazed me that I slept because I had an upset stomach all night and bad dreams and I was cold. And every time I woke up I said to myself, "What am I doing here?" But I slept most of the time even though it seemed that I was up most of the time.

"Good," he answered, trying to talk and not be up at the same time.

"I slept good, but now I'm up," I said, bugging him on purpose. I may have been kind to him at night even though he was a lousy lover, but in the morning the sight of him lying there disgusted me. Those are the cold facts. "What should I do now that I'm up?"

"Whatever you want to do, dammit!" He dragged the pillow over his head.

"I want to take a shower." I wanted to get warm. There was no steam in his cheap place.

"There is no shower!"

"Say, why don't you get up and we'll go out to a nice heated restaurant for breakfast."

He pulled the pillow over his head.

"Don't you have to get up?" I shouted into the pillow. I tried to pull it off.

"I don't ever have to get up. Go away so I can sleep."

I began to stroke his body through the sheet. When reason doesn't work, when threats go unanswered, I head for the body. "You know, you don't have any ass. That's very nice . . . your long back goes right into your long legs. You have a long face too, and the biggest forehead

I ever did see." I kissed the back of his head. He had thrown the pillow aside. "Paul, please get up so that we can be friends. If you don't get up I'm liable to get back in bed myself and sleep the whole day. I have to fight it. Please. It's so depressing to be the only one awake." I went to the window and rubbed my name into the dirty pane. I was always writing my name on things, as if I wasn't sure who I was. Like I wouldn't be thinking about it and suddenly there it was, in water, in dust, in sand, on someone's back, on a steamed mirror . . . my name. And there it was in city dust, ROSA. The dirt in the country is cleaner. I went to Canada once and camped out for two days without any clothes on.

"Hand me my glasses," Paul said. "Next to the clock." He groped for his glasses, his arms rising out of the sea for the last time. I slapped them into his hand, a magician's assistant.

"The object you are are holding, doctor . . . can you tell me something about its owner?"

"The owner of these eyeglasses is almost totally blind without them. With them he can see to the ends of the earth and back, although he hasn't gotten back yet."

"Bravo doctor!" I gave him a big hug. "You know, you can be fun if you try."

"Get dressed, I'll take you out to eat and then to the Museum of Modern Art."

That was groovy. I had been thinking of splitting and just standing around Washington Square Park eating candied violets. Actually the idea of going to a museum wasn't too exciting. Not that all museums bore me. I dig the Indian museum in Washington Heights— lots of bones and jewelry, and pottery, and feathers! The feathers are best: turquoise, orange, yellow! But then the bird can't fly. I gave Paul a button. I said, "Here's a button for you. I don't wear it because it's too obvious, I mean I don't want to attract attention, but the way you look you could wear it." I pinned it on his T-shirt. It was a white button in the center of which was a drawing of the world on a globe. Above the globe it said:

THE WHOLE WORLD

Below the globe it said:

IS GOING TO POT

I'm sure Paul thought it was stupid of me, but wherever I go I leave something.

"Don't you think what it says is like 'REPENT! THE END OF THE WORLD IS AT HAND'? Look, this is my hand. I hold it out. My fingers are at the end of my hand. I touch you. You are at hand. You are the end of the world. Because the end of the world is at hand."

He responded to this by putting three of my fingers into his mouth and sucking on them. Only a Zen master would have done that.

VII

BEING A CRITIC, I have a pass to get into the museum free, but I wanted to impress Rosa, show her I wasn't afraid to dare. That I too could buck the authorities. "I have a way to get in free," I said. "Just watch me." Near the stairs on the left, about twelve feet behind the ticket-taker, is a velvet rope. I stood close to it for about two minutes, establishing my presence in that area. I then whipped one leg over the rope straddling it for an instant. My other leg followed, and then I remained stationary at the rope. I was now in. Any casual observer would have thought I had never moved from that spot. "Okay, now you," I whispered to Rosa. "It's easy, come on. They shouldn't charge admission anyway." She couldn't move. She felt she was being watched. I didn't expect it of her. I thought she would enjoy getting away with something. I got sore at her. "Shit, what's taking so long? Don't you trust me?" I reached over and tugged at her sleeve. She pulled in the other direction.

"I can't," she said, and bought a ticket to get in. She used two Kennedy half-dollars, which she said she had been saving in case their value went up like Mickey Mouse watches. I was furious.

"You're trying to make a fool of me," I said. I felt like

choking her. I can't bear to have anyone pit their will
against mine.

"It's your trip, Paul, you take it." Then she said, "Don't
try to carry me under your coat or stuff me under your
seat, dig?"

"You don't have money to waste!" I shrieked stupidly,
hoping she would recognize the essentially sacred character of money.

"Money is to use!" she answered.

"Use your brains," I answered.

"Use yours! I mean how can I dig the museum if I get
uptight trying to sneak in?"

"I thought you were cool," I said disdainfully.

"What gave you that idea, my long hair and boots?"

"Forgive and forget." I then said, "Let's continue as if
it had never happened." It satisfied me to incite anger in
Rosa and then just leave her boiling. I thought she might
get physical. But I was to be deprived. All she said was:

"Okay."

VIII

I GLANCED at Paul. His face was white. I felt bad for
him. I offered him a slice of rose-hip gum. Maybe he
needed Vitamin C. He began steering me around the
museum by my shoulders. He handled me like a dummy
on a dolly. Ridiculous, the way he treated me like a pupil.
He was so serious. Art was heavy to him, man! It weighed
a ton. He didn't know that I don't learn much. Especially
when someone sinks into my shoulders and forces education on me.

". . . Rousseau . . ." Paul said. I don't know what
else.

But I looked and made up my own mind. "Outta sight!
That stiff little sheik sleeping in the desert with a lion
guarding him! I guess the lion isn't hungry, or maybe a
guy in a helicopter shot it with a tranquilizer dart. And
dig that striped shawl! I had one once. When they get
dirty you wash them in cold salty water."

"Rousseau was a primitive like you," Paul said. "No detail escaped him. The dream was real to Rousseau."

"What was he on?" I asked, to bug my instructor.

"I don't believe he used drugs, but Modigliani did. First to execute his work, then to execute himself. Blind, he stumbled into self-death."

I began to applaud. It embarrassed Paul. He hadn't realized (or had he?) how overblown he sounded. God, "Blind, he stumbled into self-death!" "Do you know any artists I can pose for?" I asked. Paul let it pass. One night with him and I could tell he thought he owned me. And he didn't particularly like to see my body anyway. It didn't occur to him that posing was just a job to me and I needed one. Why did he think I spent my Kennedy half-dollars!

As many artists as Paul probably knew who lived badly and were unhappy, I guess he imagined that they were the swingers, the true and natural lovers of women. That they actually fucked with the brush.

That "they" could get it up for any female no matter what her score on the strength-o-meter, while he required special conditions. He took me out into the garden. I didn't ask him about modeling again.

We stood in front of the Lachaise lady and Paul said, "Isn't that monumental? Notice the material flowing but controlled, commanding the space around her. He used his wife as a model. Idealized her. There are drawings in which her breasts fly out behind her like wings and her ass becomes widened and flattened—a plateau of joy. Notice the small graceful head held high. Notice the narrow extremities. Poised on her toes she swells upward, but always anchored. Perfectly balanced. However, when we get home I'll show you a photograph in which she floats like a marble cloud."

"Idealized fat!" I said. "She must have had a lot of money for him to have married her."

"Don't be dumb," Paul said.

"Okay, I won't be dumb." I let my fingers run down one smooth bronze thigh. "I slept with a sculptor once and he showed me pictures of some Italian sculptor's work, the

statues were very thin—thin, long, and bumpy, and ugly.
Well, his statue people were kind of walking and standing
still at the same time. I hated those sculptures too. So it
doesn't matter to me whether the figure is fat or skinny;
if something is exaggerated I hate it. Do I look like that
. . . exaggerated?"

"You're not long and bumpy, luckily," Paul said, rest-
ing his hand on my hip. He massaged it and patted it.
Then his hand dropped to his side. "The artist whose
work you hate so much was called Giacometti. He considered his work unfinished, continually changing, almost
skeletal . . . shedding plaster like rotting flesh."

"It looked it," I said. "Know what?"

"What?" Paul asked.

"I'd like some groovy oatmeal with honey and lime."

"We'll buy some and you can come home with me and
cook it." The museum was getting on Paul's nerves. He
must have been thinking, "Art is dead." That's what I was
thinking. Then something caught my eye.

"What's that?" I pinched his arm very hard and made
him wince.

"What's what?"

"What's that hairless, armless, walking chromium man
with a can on his chest? New concept in heart transplant?"

"Trova did that one."

"Lots of Italian artists, right? I have Italian blood in me.
Jewish-Italian. That's why I'm so emotional."

"You're Jewish-Italian?" He didn't believe me.

"I think so, because I sing and dance and love and hate,
and when I'm not doing that I'm bored. Man, I've got to
be freaked out all the the time because that's the way I am.
You're the freakiest thing I've ever done, Paul. Honest, it
goes against my Italian-Jewish blood. We don't communi-
cate. You're the uppest tightest cat I ever did meet. Or am
I paranoid? That's it. I must be paranoid. You're in this
art bag with the other peanuts, and here I am trying to
get in, or grab one, so I make believe all your peanuts are
bad. Dig? Or I make believe all your peanuts are shells . . .
So don't hate me because I'm Italian-Jewish. Hate me because I love hot roasted peanuts." I didn't know at all what

I meant, but it seemed to make sense and Paul thought it was very funny. I was also pulling him along.

"Rosa, you have more force and pull than mother moon. Look at the water in the pool. It's lapping in your direction. You've brought on high tide. Only the moon and Busby Berkeley can do that."

I glanced down at what he called water. "That's water? It's gray as granite. They should put orange or pink dye in it. I'll bet people fall in. People who can't swim."

"Do you swim?" Paul asked.

"Sure I swim," I answered. "I love being wet. It's so sexy being wet with clothes on. Your nipples stick out, and the belly button makes its own tiny pool. And your hair becomes a helmet dripping gems of water like one of those Japanese beaded curtains. Coming out of the water is like being in a silent movie."

"I don't like being wet," Paul said.

Man, it was as if he was defending himself from wetting his bed. "You must have had a rough time in the womb. Your mother must have been on a roller coaster all the time." I sat down on the steps leading to the garden. A guard snapped his fingers at me. I stood up and in half a second flipped my breast out and back into my blouse. Only the guard and Paul saw it. "Far out! Now he doesn't know if he's dreaming or not. He shouldn't have snapped his fingers at me. Nobody's gonna fall over me on the steps. They can see me."

"There are chairs over there," Paul said. He was dying.

"I'm not over there, I'm here. You talk just like the establishment. How did you like the speedy tit? Shocking, huh? When I have a baby I'm gonna hang him on my tit wherever I go. I love having my breasts sucked on. It separates the women from the tight little sandpaper cunts, right?"

"Rosa, let's go," Paul begged. "I want to get you that oatmeal, lime, and honey—and some bells, because I think people should be warned when you're coming."

Paul showed me his museum pass when we got outside.

"Why didn't you use it?" I asked.

"I like to live dangerously," he said.

"You're one big surprise after another, aren't you?" I

said, having had bigger surprises than him in my lifetime, but also humoring him. "You know what?—it's cool so long as you don't get caught. Do anything you want, but don't get caught!" We linked arms, took big steps, and cheerfully bounced our way toward the Avenue of the Americas.

Atavist

Hugh Seidman

Venturing to the world:
the doctor's office.

The civilized diseases:
gonorrhea, falling hair,
bad skin, neurasthenia.

Body edging into spirit
and I debate:
Is it moral to get better?

St. Francis kissed that leper,
who disdained him,
cursed and dragged off,
jangling his bell on the landscape.

Illumination Rounds

Michael Herr

WE WERE ALL strapped into the seats of the Chinook, fifty of us, and something, someone, was hitting it from the outside with an enormous hammer. *How do they do that,* I thought, *we're a thousand feet in the air!* But it had to be that, over and over, shaking the helicopter, making it dip and turn in a horrible out-of-control motion that took me in the stomach. I had to laugh, it was so exciting, it was the thing I had wanted, almost what I had wanted except for that wrenching, resonant metal-echo; I could hear it even above the noise of the rotor blades. And they were going to fix that, I knew they would make it stop. They had to, it was going to make me sick.

They were all replacements going in to mop up after the big battles on Hills 875 and 876, the battles that had already taken on the name of one great battle, the Battle of Dakto. And I was new, brand-new, three days in-country, embarrassed about my boots because they were so new. And across from me, ten feet away, a boy tried to jump out of the straps and then jerked forward and hung there, his rifle barrel caught in the red plastic webbing of the seat-back. As the chopper rose again and turned, his weight went back hard against the webbing and a dark spot the size of a baby's hand showed in the center of his fatigue jacket. And it grew—I knew what it was, but not really—it got up to his armpits and then started down his sleeves and up over his shoulders at the same time. It went all across his waist and down his legs, covering the canvas on his boots until they were dark like everything else he wore, and it was running in slow, heavy drops off of his fingertips. I thought I could hear the drops hitting the metal strip on the chopper floor. Hey! . . . oh, but this isn't anything at all, it's not real, it's just some *thing* they're going through that isn't real. One of the door gunners was heaped up on the floor like a cloth dummy. His hand had the bloody raw look of a pound of liver fresh from the butcher paper. We touched down on the same LZ we had left just a few minutes before, but I didn't know it until one of the guys shook my shoulder, and then I couldn't stand up. All I could feel of my legs was their shaking, and the guy thought I'd been hit and helped me up. The chopper had taken eight hits, there was shattered plastic all over the floor, a dying pilot up front, and the boy was hanging forward in the straps again; he was dead, but not (I knew) really dead.

It took me a month to lose that feeling of being a spectator to something that was part game, part show. That first afternoon, before I'd boarded the Chinook, a black sergeant had tried to keep me from going. He told me I was too new to go near the kind of shit they were throwing around up in those hills. ("You a reporter?" he'd asked, and I'd said, "No, a writer," dumbass and pompous, and he'd laughed and said, "Careful. You can't use no eraser up where you wanna go.") He'd pointed to the bodies of all the dead Americans lined in two long rows near the chopper pad, so many that they could not even cover all of them decently. But they were not real then, and taught me nothing. The Chinook had come in, blowing my helmet off, and I grabbed it up and joined the replacements waiting to board. "Okay, man," the sergeant said. "You gotta go, you gotta go. All's I can say is, I hope you get a clean wound."

●

THE BATTLE for Hill 875 was over, and some survivors were being brought in by Chinook to the landing strip at Dakto. The 173rd Airborne had taken over 400 casualties, nearly 200 killed, most of them on the previous afternoon and in the fighting that had gone on all through the

night. It was very cold and wet up there, and some Red
Cross girls had been sent up from Pleiku to comfort
the survivors. As the troops filed out of the helicopters,
the girls waved and smiled at them from behind their
serving tables. "Hi soldier! What's your name?" "Where
you from, soldier?" "I'll bet some hot coffee would hit the
spot about now."

And the men from the 173rd just kept walking without
answering, staring straight ahead, their eyes rimmed with
red from fatigue, their faces pinched and aged with all
that had happened during the night. One of them dropped
out of line and said something to a loud, fat girl who wore
a Peanuts sweatshirt under her fatigue blouse, and she
started to cry. The rest just walked past the girls and the
large, olive-drab coffee urns. They had no idea of where
they were.

●

AT ONE TIME they would have lighted your cigarette
for you on the terrace of the Continental Hotel. But those
days are almost twenty years gone, and anyway, who
really misses them? Now there is a crazy American who
looks like George Orwell, and he is always sleeping off
his drinks in one of the wicker chairs there, slumped
against a table, starting up with violence, shouting and
then going back to sleep. He makes everyone nervous,
especially the waiters: the old ones who had served the
French and the Japanese and the first American journalists
and O.S.S. types ("Those noisy bastards at the Continental," Graham Greene called them.) and the really young
ones who bussed the tables and pimped in a modest way.
The little elevator boy still greets the guests each morning
with a quiet "Ça va?", but he is seldom answered, and
the old baggage man (he also brings us grass) will sit in
the lobby and say, "How are you tomorrow?"

"The Ballad of Billy Joe" plays from speakers mounted
on the terrace's corner columns, but the air seems too
heavy to carry the sound right, and it hangs in the corners. There is an exhausted, drunk master sergeant from
the First Infantry Division who has bought a flute from

the old man in khaki shorts and pith helmet who sells instruments along Tu Do Street. The old man will lean over the butt-strewn flower boxes that line the terrace and play "Frère Jacques" on a wooden stringed instrument. The sergeant has bought the flute, and he is playing it quietly, pensively, badly.

The tables are crowded with American civilian construction engineers, men getting $30,000 a year from their jobs on government contracts and matching that easily on the black market. Their faces have the look of aerial photos of silicone pits, all hung with loose flesh and standing veins. Their mistresses were among the prettiest, saddest girls in Vietnam. I always wondered what they had looked like before they'd made their arrangements with the engineers. You'd see them at the tables there, smiling their hard, empty smiles into those rangy, brutal, scared faces. No wonder those men all looked alike to the Vietnamese; after awhile, they all looked alike to me. Out on the Bien Hoa Highway, north of Saigon, there is a monument to the Vietnamese war dead, and it is one of the few graceful things left in the country. It is a modest pagoda set above the road and approached by long flights of gently rising steps. One Sunday, I saw a bunch of these engineers gunning their Harleys up those steps, laughing and shouting in the afternoon sun. The Vietnamese had a special name for them to distinguish them from all other Americans; it translated out to something like "The Terrible Ones," although I'm told that this doesn't even approximate the odium carried in the original.

●

THERE WAS a young sergeant in the Special Forces, stationed at the C Detachment in Can Tho that served as the SF headquarters for IV Corps. In all, he had spent thirty-six months in Vietnam. This was his third extended tour, and he planned to come back again as soon as he possibly could after this current hitch was finished. During his last tour, he had lost a finger and part of a thumb in a firefight, and he had been generally shot up enough times for the three Purple Hearts which mean that you don't have to fight in Vietnam anymore. After all that, I guess they thought of him as a combat liability, but he was such a hard-charger that they gave him the EM Club to manage. He ran it well and seemed happy, except that he had gained a lot of weight in the duty, and it set him apart from the rest of the men. He loved to horse around with the Vietnamese in the compound, leaping on them from behind, leaning heavily on them, shoving them around and pulling their ears, sometimes punching them a little hard in the stomach, smiling a stiff small smile that was meant to tell them all that he was just being playful. The Vietnamese would smile too, until he turned to walk away. He loved the Vietnamese, he said, he really *knew* them after three years. As far as he was concerned, there was no place in the world as fine as Vietnam. And back home in North Carolina, he had a large, glass-covered display case in which he kept his medals and decorations and citations, the photographs taken during three tours and countless battles, letters from past commanders, a few souvenirs. The case stood in the center of the living room, he said, and every night his wife and three kids would move the kitchen table out in front of it and eat their dinner there.

●

At eight hundred feet we knew we were being shot at. Something hit the underside of the chopper but did not penetrate it. They weren't firing tracers, but we saw the brilliant flickering blips of light below, and the pilot circled and came down very fast, working the button that released fire from the flex guns mounted on either side of the Huey. Every fifth round was a tracer, and they sailed out and down, incomparably graceful, closer and closer, until they met the tiny point of light coming from the jungle. The ground fire stopped, and we went on to land at Vinh Long, where the pilot yawned and said, "I think I'll go to bed early tonight and see if I can wake up with any enthusiasm for this war."

●

A TWENTY-FOUR-YEAR-OLD Special Forces captain
was telling me about it. "I went out and killed one VC
and liberated a prisoner. Next day the major called me in
and told me that I'd killed fourteen VC and liberated six
prisoners. You want to see the medal?"

●

THERE WAS a little air-conditioned restaurant on the
corner of Le-Loi and Tu Do, across from the Continental
Hotel and the old opera house which now served as the
Vietnamese Lower House. Some of us called it the Graham
Greene Milk Bar (a scene in "The Quiet American" had
taken place there), but its name was Givral. Every morning, they baked their own *baguettes* and *croissants*, and
the coffee wasn't too bad. Sometimes I'd meet there with
a friend of mine for breakfast.

He was a Belgian, a tall, slow-moving man of thirty
who'd been born in the Congo. He professed to know and
love war, and he affected the mercenary sensibility. He'd
been photographing the Vietnam thing for seven or eight
years now, and once in a while he'd go over to Laos and
run around the jungles there with the government, search-
ing for the dreaded Pathet Lao, which he pronounced
"Paddy Lao." Other people's stories of Laos always made
it sound like a lotus-land where no one wanted to hurt anyone, but he said that whenever he went on ops there he
always kept a grenade taped to his belly because he was
a Catholic and knew what the Paddy Lao would do to
him if he were captured. But he was a little crazy that
way, and tended to dramatize his war stories.

He always wore dark glasses, probably even during
operations. His pictures sold to the wire services, and I
saw a few of them in the American news magazines. He
was very kind in a gruff, off-handed sort of way; kindness
embarrassed him, and he was so graceless among people,
so eager to shock, that he couldn't understand why so
many of us liked him. Irony was the effect he worked

for in conversation, that and a sense of how exquisite the war could be when all of its machinery was running right. He was explaining the finish of an operation he'd just been on in War Zone C, above Cu Chi.

"There were a lot of dead VC," he said. "Dozens and dozens of them! A lot of them were from that same village that has been giving you so much trouble lately. VC from top to bottom—Michael, in that village the fucking *ducks* are VC. So the American commander had twenty or thirty of the dead flown up in a sling-load and dropped into the village. I should say it was a drop of at least two hundred feet, all those dead Vietcongs, right in the middle of the village."

He smiled (I couldn't see his eyes).

"Ah, Psywar!" he said, kissing off the tips of his fingers.

●

Bob Stokes of *Newsweek* told me this: In the big Marine hospital in Danang, they have what is called the "White Lie Ward," where they bring some of the worst cases, the ones that can be saved but who will never be the same again. A young Marine was carried in, still unconscious and full of morphine, and his legs were gone. As he was being carried into the ward, he came to briefly and saw a Catholic chaplain standing over him.

"Father," he said, "am I all right?"

The chaplain didn't know what to say. "You'll have to talk about that with the doctors, son."

"Father, are my legs okay?"

"Yes," the chaplain said. "Sure."

By the next afternoon the shock had worn off, and the boy knew all about it. He was lying on his cot when the chaplain came by.

"Father," the Marine said, "I'd like to ask you for something."

"What, son?"

"I'd like to have that cross." And he pointed to the tiny silver insignia on the chaplain's lapel.

"Of course," the chaplain said. "But why?"

"Well, it was the first thing I saw when I came to yesterday, and I'd like to have it."

The chaplain removed the cross and handed it to him. The Marine held it tightly in his fist and looked at the chaplain.

"You lied to me, Father," he said. "You cocksucker. You lied to me."

•

His name was Davies, and he was a gunner with a helicopter group based at Tan Son Nhut airport. On paper, by the regulations, he was billeted in one of the big "hotel" BEQs in Cholon, but he only kept his things there. He actually lived in a small two-story Vietnamese house deeper inside of Cholon, as far from the papers and the regulations as he could get. Every morning he took an Army bus with wire-grill windows out to the base and flew missions, mostly around War Zone C, along the Cambodian border, and most nights he returned to the house in Cholon where he lived with his "wife" (he'd found her in one of the bars) and some other Vietnamese who were said to be the girl's family. Her mamma-san and her brother were always there, living on the first floor, and there were others who came and went. He seldom saw the brother, but every few days he would find a pile of labels and brand names torn from cardboard cartons, American products that the brother wanted from the PX.

The first time I saw him he was sitting alone at a table on the Continental terrace, drinking a beer. He had a full, drooping moustache and sharp, sad eyes, and he was wearing a denim workshirt and wheat jeans. He also carried a Leica and a copy of *Ramparts Magazine*, and I just assumed at first that he was a correspondent. I didn't know then that you could buy *Ramparts* at the PX, and after I'd borrowed and returned it, we began to talk. It was the issue that featured left-wing Catholics like Jesus Christ and Fulton Sheen on the cover. "*Catholique?*" one of the bar girls said later that night. "*Moi aussi,*" and she kept the magazine. That was when we were walking around Cholon in the rain trying to find

Hoa, his wife. Mamma-san had told us that she'd gone to the movies with some girl friends, but Davies knew what she was doing.

"I hate that shit," he said. "It's so uncool."

"Well, don't put up with it."

"Yeah."

Davies' house was down a long narrow alley that became nothing more than a warren at the end, smelling of camphor-smoke and fish, crowded but clean. He would not speak to Mamma-san, and we walked straight up to the second floor. It was one long room that had a sleeping area screened off in an arrangement of filmy curtains. At the top of the stairs there was a large poster of Lenny Bruce, and beneath it, in a shrine effect, was a low table with a Buddha and lighted incense on it.

"Lenny," Davies said.

Most of one wall was covered with a collage that Davies had done with the help of some friends. It included photos of burning monks, stacked Vietcong dead, wounded Marines screaming and weeping, Cardinal Spellman waving from a chopper, Ronald Reagan, his face halved and separated by a stalk of cannabis; pictures of John Lennon peering through wire-rimmed glasses, Mick Jagger, Jimi Hendrix, Dylan, Eldridge Cleaver, Rap Brown; coffins draped with American flags whose stars were replaced by swastikas and dollar signs; odd parts clipped from *Playboy* pictures, newspaper headlines (Farmers Butcher Hogs to Protest Pork Price Dip), photo captions (President Jokes with Newsmen), beautiful girls holding flowers, showers of peace symbols; Ky standing at attention and saluting, a small mushroom cloud forming where his genitalia should have been; a map of the Western United States with the shape of Vietnam reversed and fitted over California and one large, long figure that began at the bottom with shiny leather boots and rouged knees and ascended in a microskirt, bare breasts, graceful shoulders, and a long neck, topped by the burned, blackened face of a dead Vietnamese woman.

By the time Davies' friends showed up, we were already stoned. We could hear them below, laughing and rapping with Mamma, and then they came up the stairs, three blacks and two white guys.

"It sure do smell *peculiar* up here," one of them said.

"Hi, you freaky li'l fuckers."

"This grass is Number Ten," Davies said. "Every time I smoke this grass over here it gives me a bad trip."

"Ain' nuthin' th' matter with that grass," someone said. "It ain' the grass."

"Where's Hoa?"

"Yeah, Davies, where's your ole lady at?"

"She's out hustling Saigon tea, and I'm fucking sick of it." He tried to look really angry, but he only looked unhappy.

One of them handed off a joint and stretched out. "Hairy day today," he said.

"Where'd you fly?"

"Bu Dop."

"Bu Dop!" one of the spades said, and he started to move toward the joint, jiving and working his shoulders, bopping his head. "Bu Dop, budop, bu dop dop *dop!*"

"Funky funky Bu Dop."

"Hey, man, can you O.D. on grass?"

"I dunno, baby. Maybe we could get jobs at the Aberdeen Proving Grounds smokin' dope for Uncle Sugar."

"Wow, I'm stoned. Hey, Davies, you stoned?"

"Yeah," Davies said.

It started to rain again, so hard that you couldn't hear drops, only the full force of the water pouring down on the metal roof. We smoked a little more, and then the others started to leave. Davies looked like he was sleeping with his eyes open.

"That goddam pig," he said. "Fuckin' whore. Man, I'm paying out all this bread for the house, and those people downstairs. I don't even know who they are, for Christ's sake. I'm really . . . I'm getting sick of it."

"You're pretty short now," someone said. "Why don't you cut out?"

"You mean just split?"

"Why not?"

Davies was quiet for a long time.

"Yeah," he finally said. "This is bad. This is really bad. I think I'm going to get out of here."

A BIRD COLONEL, commanding a brigade of the 4th Infantry Division: "I'll bet you always wondered why we call 'em Dinks up in this part of the country. I thought of it myself. I'll tell you, I never *did* like hearing them called Charlie. See, I had an uncle named Charlie, and I liked him, too. No, Charlie was just too damn good for the little bastards. So I just thought, What are they *really* like? and I came up with rinky-dink. Suits 'em just perfect, Rinky-Dink, 'cause that's what they are. 'Cept that was too long, so we cut it down some. And that's why we call 'em Dinks."

●

ONE MORNING BEFORE DAWN, Ed Fouhy, a former Saigon bureau chief for CBS, went out to the 8th Aerial Port at Tan Son Nhut to catch the early military flight to Danang. They boarded as the sun came up, and Fouhy strapped in next to a kid in rumpled fatigues, one of those soldiers you see whose weariness has gone far beyond physical exhaustion, into that state where no amount of sleep will give them the kind of rest they need. Every torpid movement they make tells you that they are tired, that they'll stay tired until their tours are up and the big bird flies them back to the World. Their eyes are dim with it, their faces almost puffy, and when they smile, you have to accept it as a token.

There was a standard question you could use to open a conversation with troops, and Fouhy tried it. "How long you been in-country?" he asked.

The kid half-lifted his head; that question could *not* be serious. The weight was really on him, and the words came slowly:

"All . . . fuckin' . . . day," he said.

●

You GUYS ought do a story on me suntahm," the kid said. He was a helicopter gunner, six-three with an enormous head that sat in bad proportion to the rest of his body and a line of picket teeth that were always on show in a wet, uneven smile. Every few seconds he would have to wipe his mouth with the back of his hand, and when he talked to you his face was always an inch from yours, so that I had to take my glasses off to keep them dry. He was from Kilgore, Texas, and he was on his seventeenth consecutive month in-country.

"Why should we do a story about you?"

"'Cause I'm so fuckin' good," he said, "'n' that ain' no shit, neither. Got me one hunnert 'n' fifty-se'en gooks kilt. 'N' fifty caribou." He grinned and stanched the saliva for a second. "Them're all certified," he added.

The chopper touched down at Ba Xoi and we got off, not unhappy about leaving him. "Lis'n," he said, laughing, "you git up onna ridgeline, see y' keep yer head down. Y'heah?"

●

SAY; how'd you get to be a co-respondent an' come ovah to this raggedy-ass motherfucker?"

He was a really big spade, rough-looking even when he smiled, and he wore a gold nose-bead fastened through his left nostril. I told him that the nose-bead blew my mind, and he said that was all right, it blew everybody's mind. We were sitting by the chopper pad of an LZ above Kontum. He was trying to get to Dakto, I was heading for Pleiku, and we both wanted to get out of there before nightfall. We took turns running out to the pad to check the choppers that kept coming in and taking off, neither of us were having any luck, and after we'd talked for an hour he laid a joint on me and we smoked.

"I been heah mo'n eight months now," he said. "I bet I been in mo'n twenny firefights. An' I ain' hardly fired back once."

"How come?"

"Shee-it, I go firin' back, I might kill one a th' Brothers, you dig it?"

I nodded, no Vietcong ever called *me* honky, and he told me that in his company alone there were more than a dozen Black Panthers, and that he was one of them. I didn't say anything, and then he said that he wasn't just a Panther; he was an agent for the Panthers, sent over here to recruit. I asked him what kind of luck he'd been having, and he said fine, real fine. There was a fierce wind blowing across the LZ, and the joint didn't last very long.

"Hey baby," he said. "That was jes' some jive I tole you. Shit, I ain' no Panther. I'se jes' fuckin' with you, see what you'd say."

"But the Panthers have guys over here. I've met some."

"Tha' could be," he said, and he laughed.

A Huey came in, and he jogged out to see where it was headed. It was going to Dakto, and he came back to get his gear. "Later, baby," he said. "An' luck." He jumped into the chopper, and as it rose from the strip he leaned out and laughed, bringing his arm up and bending it back towards him, palm out and the fist clenched tightly in the Sign.

●

ONE DAY I went out with the ARVN on an operation in the rice paddies above Vinh Long, forty terrified Vietnamese troops and five Americans, all packed into three Hueys that dropped us up to our hips in paddy muck. I had never been in a rice paddy before. We spread out and moved toward the marshy swale that led to the jungle. We were still twenty feet from the first cover, a low paddy wall, when we took fire from the treeline. It was probably the working half of a crossfire that had somehow gone wrong. It caught one of the ARVN in the head, and he dropped back into the water and disappeared. We made it to the wall with two casualties. There was no way of stopping their fire, no room to send out a flanking party, so gunships were called in and we crouched behind the wall and waited. There was a lot of fire coming from the trees, but we were all right as long as we kept down. And I was thinking, Oh man, so this is a rice paddy, yes, wow! when I suddenly heard an electric guitar shooting right up into my ear and a mean, rapturous black voice singing, coaxing, "Now c'mon baby, stop actin' so crazy," and when I got it all together I turned to see a grinning black corporal hunched over a casette recorder. "Might's well," he said. "We ain' goin' nowhere till them gunships come."

That's the story of the first time I ever heard Jimi Hendrix, but in a war where a lot of people talked about Aretha's "Satisfaction" the way other people speak of Brahms' Fourth, it was more than a story; it was Credentials. "Say, that Jimi Hendrix is my main man," someone would say. "He has *definitely* got his shit together!" Hendrix had once been in the 101st Airborne, and the Airborne in Vietnam was full of wiggy-brilliant spades like him, really mean and really good, guys who always took care of you when things got bad. That music meant a lot to them. I never once heard it played over the Armed Forces Radio Network.

●

THE SERGEANT had lain out near the clearing for almost two hours with a wounded medic. He had called over and over for a Medevac, but none had come. Finally, a chopper from another outfit, an LOH, appeared, and he was able to reach it by radio. The pilot told him that he'd have to wait for one of his own ships, they weren't coming down, and the sergeant told the pilot that if he did not land for them he was going to open fire on them from the ground and fucking well *bring* him down. So they were picked up that way, but there were repercussions.

The commander's code name was Mal Hombre, and he reached the sergeant later that afternoon from a place with the call signal Violent Meals.

"God *damn* it, Sergeant," he said through the static. "I thought you were a professional soldier."

"I waited as long as I could, sir. Any longer, I was gonna lose my man."

"This outfit is perfectly capable of taking care of its own dirty laundry. Is that clear, Sergeant?"

"Colonel, since when is a wounded trooper 'dirty laundry'?"

"At ease, Sergeant," Mal Hombre said, and radio contact was broken.

●

THERE WAS a spec 4 in the Special Forces at Can Tho, a shy Indian boy from Chinle, Arizona, with large, wet eyes the color of ripe olives and a quiet way of speaking, a really nice way of putting things, kind to everyone without ever being stupid or soft about it. On the night that the compound and the airstrip were hit, he came and asked me if there was a chaplain anywhere around. He wasn't very religious, he said, but he was worried about tonight. He'd just volunteered for a "suicide squad," two jeeps that were going to drive across the airstrip with mortars and a recoilless rifle. It looked bad, I had to admit it; there were so few of us in the compound that they'd had to put me on the reaction force. It might be bad. He just had a feeling about it, he'd seen what always happened to guys whenever they got that feeling, at least he *thought* it was that feeling, a bad one, the worst he'd ever had.

I told him that the only chaplains I could think of would be in the town, and we both knew that the town was cut off.

"Oh," he said. "Look then. If I get it tonight . . ."

"It'll be okay."

"Listen, though. If it happens . . . I think it's going to . . . Will you make sure the colonel tells my folks I was looking for a chaplain, anyway?"

I promised, and the jeeps loaded and drove off. I heard later that there had been a brief firefight, but that no one had been hurt. They didn't have to use the recoilless. They all drove back into the compound two hours later. The next morning at breakfast, he sat at another table, saying a lot of loud, brutal things about the gooks, and he wouldn't look at me. But at noon he came over and squeezed my arm and smiled, his eyes fixed somewhere just to the right of my own.

●

FOR TWO DAYS NOW, ever since the Tet Offensive had begun, they had been coming by the hundreds to the province hospital at Can Tho. They were usually either very young or very old or women, and their wounds were often horrible. The more lightly wounded were being treated quickly in the hospital yard, and the more serious cases were simply placed in one of the corridors to die. There were just too many of them to treat, the doctors had worked without a break, and now, on the second afternoon, the Vietcong began shelling the hospital.

One of the Vietnamese nurses handed me a cold can of beer and asked me to take it down the hall, where one of the Army surgeons was operating. The door of the room was ajar, and I walked right in. I probably should have looked first. A little girl was lying on the table, looking with wide dry eyes at the wall. Her left leg was gone, and a sharp piece of bone about six inches long extended from the exposed stump. The leg itself was on the floor, half wrapped in a piece of paper. The doctor was a major, and he'd been working alone. He could not have looked worse if he'd lain all night in a trough of blood. His hands were so slippery that I had to hold the can to his mouth for him and tip it up as his head went back. I couldn't look at the girl.

"Is it all right?" he said quietly.

"It's okay now. I expect I'll be sick as hell later on."

He placed his hand on the girl's forehead and said, "Hello, little darling." He thanked me for bringing the beer. He probably thought that he was smiling, but nothing changed anywhere in his face. He'd been working this way for nearly twenty hours.

●

THE COURTYARD of the American compound in Hue was filled with puddles from the rain, and the canvas tops of the jeeps and trucks sagged with the weight of the water. It was the fifth day of the fighting, and everyone was still amazed that the NVA or the Cong had not hit the compound on the first night. An enormous white goose had come into the compound that night, and now his wings were heavy with the oil that had formed on the surface of the puddles. Every time a vehicle entered the yard he would beat his wings in a fury and scream, but he never left the compound and, as far as I knew, no one ever ate him.

Nearly two hundred of us were sleeping in the two small rooms that had been the compound's dining quarters. The Army was not happy about having to billet all of the Marines that were coming through, and they were absolutely furious about all of the correspondents who were hanging around, waiting until the fighting moved north across the river, into the Citadel. You were lucky to find space enough on the floor to lie down on, luckier if you found an empty stretcher to sleep on, and luckiest of all if the stretcher was new. All night long the few unbroken windows would rattle from the airstrikes across the river, and a mortar pit just outside fired incessantly. At two or three in the morning, Marines would come in from their patrols. They'd cross the room, not much caring whether they stepped on anyone or not. They'd turn their radios on and shout across the room to one another. "Really, can't you fellows show a bit more consideration?" a British correspondent said, and their laughter woke anyone who was not already up.

One morning there was a fire in the prison camp across the road from the compound. We saw the black smoke rising over the barbed wire that topped the camp wall and heard automatic weapons' fire. The prison was full of captured NVA and Vietcong or Vietcong suspects; the guards said that the fire had been started to cover an escape. The ARVN and a few Americans were shooting blindly into the flames, and the bodies were burning where they fell. Civilian dead lay out on the sidewalks only a block from the compound, and the park that ran along the Perfume River was littered with dead. It was cold during those days, the sun never came out once, but the rain did things to the corpses that were worse in their way than anything the sun could have done. It was on one of those days that I realized that the only corpse I could not bear to look at would be the one I would never have to see.

●

BETWEEN THE SMOKE and the mist and the flying dust inside the Citadel, it was hard to call that hour between light and darkness a true dusk, but it was the time when a lot of us would open our C-rations. We were only meters away from the worst of the fighting, not more than a Vietnamese city block in distance, and yet civilians kept appearing, smiling, shrugging, trying to get back to their homes. The Marines would try to menace them away at rifle-point, shouting, "Di, di, *di* you sorry-ass motherfuckers, go on, get the hell away from here!", and the refugees would smile, half-bowing, and flit up one of the shattered streets. A little boy of about ten came up to a bunch of Marines from Charlie Company. He was laughing and moving his head from side to side in a funny way. The fierceness in his eyes should have told everyone what it was, but it had never occurred to most of the Grunts that a Vietnamese child could be driven mad, too, and by the time they understood it the boy had begun to go for their eyes and tear at their fatigues, spooking everyone, putting everyone really up-tight, until one of the spades grabbed him from behind and held his arms. "C'mon, poor l'il baby, 'fore one a these Grunt mothers shoots you," he said, and carried the boy to where the corpsmen were.

On the worst days, no one expected to get through it alive. A despair set in among the members of the battalion that the older ones, the veterans of two other wars, had never seen before. Once or twice, when the men from graves registration took the personal effects from the packs and pockets of dead Marines, they would find letters from home that had been delivered days before and were still unopened.

We were running some wounded onto the back of a half-ton truck, and one young Marine kept crying from his stretcher. His sergeant held both of his hands, and the Marine kept saying, "Shit, sarge, I ain' gone make it. Oh damn, I'm gone die, ain' I?" "No, you ain't gonna die, for Christ's sake," the sergeant said. "Oh yeah, sarge, yeah, I am." "Crowley," the sergeant said, "you ain't hurt that bad. I want you to just shut the fuck up. You ain't done a thing 'cept bitch ever since we got to this fuckin'

Hue City." But the sergeant didn't really know. The kid had been hit in the throat, and you couldn't tell about those. Throat wounds were bad. Everyone was afraid of throat wounds.

●

WE LUCKED OUT on our connections. At the battalion aid-station in Hue we got a chopper that carried us and a dozen dead Marines to the base at Phubai, and three minutes after we arrived there we caught a C-130 to Danang. Hitching in from the airfield, we found a Psyops official who felt sorry for us and drove us all the way to the Press Center. As we came through the gate we could see that the net was up and that the daily volley ball game between the Marines assigned to the Press Center was in progress.

"Where the hell have *you* guys been?" one of them said. We looked pretty wretched.

The inside of the dining room was freezing with air-conditioning. I sat at a table and ordered a hamburger and a Remy Martin from one of the peasant girls who worked the tables. I sat there for a couple of hours, and ordered four more hamburgers and at least a dozen brandies. (I had no idea of it until the check came.) It was not possible, it was just not possible to have been where we'd been before and to be where we were now, all in the same afternoon. One of the correspondents who had come back with me sat at another table, also by himself, and we just looked at each other, shook our heads, and laughed. I went to my room and took my boots and fatigues off, putting them under the bed where I wouldn't have to look at them. I went into the bathroom and turned on the shower. The water was hot, incredibly hot, for a moment I thought I'd gone insane from it, and I sat down on the concrete floor for a long time, shaving there, soaping myself over and over. I was using up all the hot water, I knew that, but I couldn't get interested in it. I dressed and went back to the dining room. The net was down now, and one of the Marines said hello and asked me what the movie was going to be that night. I ordered a steak and another string of brandies. Then I went to bed and smoked a joint. I was going back in the morning, I knew that, it was understood. But why was it understood? All of my stuff was in order, ready for the five o'clock wakeup. I finished the joint and shuddered off into sleep.

•

MAJOR TRONG bounced around in the seat of his jeep as it drove us over the debris scattered across the streets of Hue. His face seemed completely expressionless as we passed the crowds of Vietnamese stumbling over the fallen beams and powdered brick of their homes, but his eyes were covered by dark glasses, and it was impossible to know what he was feeling. He did not look like a victor; he was so small and limp in his seat, I was sure he was going to fly out of the jeep. His driver was a sergeant named Dang, one of the biggest Vietnamese I'd ever seen, and his English was better than the major's. The jeep would stall on rubble heaps from time to time, and Dang would turn to us and smile an apology. We were on our way to the Imperial Palace.

A month earlier, the palace grounds had been covered with dozens of NVA dead and the burned-over leavings of three weeks' siege and defense. There had been some reluctance about bombing the palace, but a lot of the bombing nearby had done heavy damage, and there had been some shelling, too. The large bronze urns were dented beyond restoring, and the rains poured through a hole in the roof of the throne room, soaking the two small thrones where the old Annamese royalty had sat. In the great hall (great when you scaled it down to the Vietnamese) the red lacquerwork on the upper walls was badly chipped, and a heavy dust covered everything. The crown of the main gate had collapsed, and in the garden the broken branches of the old cay-dai trees lay like the forms of giant insects seared in a fire, wispy, delicate, dead. It was rumored during those days that the palace was being held by a unit of student volunteers who had taken the invasion of Hue as a sign and had rushed to join the North Vietnamese. The final assault had been a

privilege reserved for a battalion of elite South Vietnamese Rangers called the Hoc Bao, the Black Panthers, but
once the walls had been taken and the grounds entered,
there was no one left inside except for the dead. They
bobbed in the moat and littered all the approaches. The
Marines moved in then, and empty ration cans and mud-
died sheets from the *Stars and Stripes* were added to the
litter. A fat Marine had his picture taken pissing into the
locked-open mouth of a decomposing North Vietnamese
soldier.

"No good," Major Trong said. "No good. Fight here
very hard, very bad."

I'd been talking to Sergeant Dang about the palace
and about the line of emperors. He seemed to know a
lot about it. We stalled one last time at the foot of a
moat bridge, and I asked him the name of the last of the
emperors to have occupied the throne. He smiled and
shrugged, not so much as though he didn't know, but
as though the answer didn't much matter.

"Major Trong is Emperor now," he said, and gunned
the jeep into the palace grounds.

•

THE INTEL REPORT lay closed on the green field
table, and someone had scrawled "What does it all mean?"
across the cover sheet. There wasn't much doubt about
who had done that; the S-2 was a known ironist. There
were so many like him, really young captains and majors
who had the wit to cut back their despair, a wedge to
set against the bitterness. What got to them sooner or later
was an inability to reconcile their love of service with their
contempt for the war, and a lot of them finally had to
resign their commissions, leave the profession.

We were sitting in the tent waiting for the rain to
stop, the major, five Grunts, and myself. The rains were
constant now, ending what had been a dry monsoon season, and you could look through the tent flap and think
about the Marines up there patrolling the hills. Someone
came in to report that one of the patrols had discovered
a small arms cache.

"An arms cache!" the major said. "What happened was, one of the Grunts was out there running around, and he tripped and fell down. That's about the only way we ever find any of this shit."

He was twenty-nine, young in rank, and this was his second tour. The time before, he had been a captain commanding a regular Marine company. He knew all about Grunts and patrols, arms caches and the value of most Intelligence.

It was cold, even in the tent, and the enlisted Marines seemed uncomfortable about lying around with a stranger, a correspondent there. The major was a cool head, they knew that; there wasn't going to be any kind of hassle until the rain stopped. They talked quietly among themselves at the far end of the tent, away from the light of the lantern. Reports kept coming in; reports from the Vietnamese, from recon, from Division, situation reports, casualty reports, three casualty reports in twenty minutes. The major looked them all over.

"Did you know that a dead Marine costs $18,000?" he said. The Grunts all turned around and looked at us. They knew how the major had meant that because they knew the major. They were just seeing about me.

The rain stopped, and they left. Outside, the air was still cool, but heavy, too, as though a terrible heat was coming on. The major and I stood by the tent and watched while an F-4 flew nose-down, released its load against the base of a hill, leveled, and flew upward again.

"I've been having this dream," the major said. "I've had it two times now. I'm in a big examination room back at Quantico. They're handing out questionnaires for an aptitude test. I take one and look at it, and the first question says, 'How many kinds of animals can you kill with your hands?' "

We could see rain falling in a sheet about a kilometer away. Judging by the wind, the major gave it three minutes before it reached us.

"After the first tour, I'd have the goddamndest nightmares. You know, the works. Bloody stuff, bad fights, guys dying, *me* dying . . . I thought they were the worst," he said. "But I sort of miss them now."

Two Poems

Lou Lipsitz

Nose

HOW POWERFUL the nose began
like a trumpet
blowing inward
and we followed its
delicate roar everywhere
over the ground

it blew the fire and smoke
into our brains
and from it, close to the forest floor,
the knowledge of decay
sank into our hearts

we were like dogs then
not hesitating to sniff
the lovely, black acidity of the genitals
and also the scattered manure of our own kind
that told us
we were not alone

but then as we stood up
it was no longer decisive
it became the joke
we came to overrule it
to pick at it to turn away from
what it told us of our own bodies:
what it is
that makes us suddenly break into a sweat

still at times
some difficult
perfume
resurrects the trumpet
and it blows into the forehead
and into the cheeks
and the skull's ancient stones
move
and the lips feel as if

they are about to grasp
a breast's milky nipple

and we follow the small general
without pants
leading
naked irregulars against
the alien, beautiful armies of uprightness.

Heart

THE HEART has medieval
persistence
and pumps out
blotchy tapestries
of thrones
and forests

to prove fidelity
it can chew up
mouthfuls
of stained glass
sending them
ringing into the blood
like
a knight falling from a turret

it never hesitates
it comprehends armor
it sustains the double beat
of the victor's horse
in the stone courtyard
of the vanquished

it is blind
and its burnt-out sockets stare
as in a starving
face at a dungeon window
yet it
survives
the rack and the whip
only to kill

itself because the lady's body
is consumed under another's hands

if allowed its own way
it will live for long periods
as an infant
but it is also
the only one
who can locate
the child quicker than the wolves.

Pasternak: In Memoriam

Apologia pro sua vita

Edward Field

PASTERNAK, I understand you now:
you were much too wise finally
to let politics interfere with your life.
You appreciated what a miracle it was
to be able to go on living at home in a world like ours
where everything threatens daily life—
invasions, wars, political purges.
You knew that the most important thing is to stay real,
at home, undisturbed, to live quietly
in comfort with a loved one,
daily routine, boring perhaps
but how deliciously, luxuriously boring—
that is all one dreams of
in the melodramatic times of revolution and dislocation.
To lead such a life
and then to put it into jeopardy for principle?
That would be a madman—
when the world takes it from you
is time enough to start acting symbolically.

Everyone wanted to use you,

even your friends, and they couldn't understand
your not standing up for your books
(that in any case were written and would live).
But when they threatened your daily life, those friends,
the life of the poet,
then they were your enemies, those stupid idealists.
Heroes are fools and there is time to be a hero perhaps:
heroes have nothing to lose,
they have not learned to make a life in the world.
Survive, survive, the poet says.
What it comes down to is that in a world like this,
and after the horrors you lived through,
when you have found a corner to live peacefully in at last
you would be out of your mind
to risk it to change the world somehow, anyhow.

Let the people whose lives are insupportable
rise against their masters
throw themselves on the barricades
be their own heroes,
not ask you to be their hero.
They will have their Great Loves in those times,
loves they hardly make love with
and rarely if ever live with,
loves that are like life's promises
never to be fulfilled
but linger as heart-filling dreams
making the rest of your life drab forever—
who needs it?

You are right:
This real person in my arms
is who I want
not the moment of passion on the barricades
not the dream of the ideal
love in a perfect world.
Survive in this world
love as you can
and go on with your work.

Don't You Wish You Were Dead

L. Woiwode

Bruce Stuttlemeyer was not well-loved in
town. He had just moved from an outlying farm into Pet-
tibone—a village in central Illinois known for its export of
peat—at the beginning of winter, and he wore bib overalls,
flannel shirts, and high hook-and-eye shoes. Though his
dress had been acceptable enough while he lived on a
farm, he was now looked upon by his seventh grade classmates as a hick. He was diminutive and thin, with an
elongated face longer than most adults', large and fleshy
lips, eyebrows so blond they were invisible, and a big gap
between his front teeth, one of which had the end broken
off. And as if all this weren't more than enough to make
him an object of derision among his classmates, who were
at one of the most sensitive and snobbish of ages, he was
uncircumcised and poorly endowed, and had picked up
the nickname of "Needledick, the canary raper." The more
he heard the name, the more wild-eyed and violent he
became, and he began to attack anybody he thought was
using it or mocking him in any way. Parents complained to
the principal that their sons were being injured at school,
and shortly after Easter vacation Bruce turned on a bully
from the eighth grade who had been taunting him for
days, and knocked him unconscious. He was expelled from
school for a week.

When Bruce's grandaunt said that she had too many cats
and wondered if Bruce and some of his nice friends couldn't
get rid of a few, he went to see Charles Neumiller, his only
acquaintance neutral enough to be called a friend. Charles,
though not an outcast, was, in his own way, nearly as

friendless as Bruce, but with him it appeared a deliberate choice; he was sullen and aloof, he read much of the time, and all he seemed to enjoy was acting the fool for girls or playing football—which he would play only if it was tackle instead of touch. Nobody in the village, of course, owned or wore equipment.

Bruce knocked on Neumiller's front door. After a long pause, it opened halfway and Charles appeared, shadowy and detached behind the screen door.

"Stuttlemeyer," he said.

"Chuck."

Charles was amazed to see Bruce at the door; he didn't know him that well, and Bruce had never been to the house.

Bruce couldn't wait to tell Charles about the cats.

They appraised one another with blank faces. Bruce, shifting his weight on his feet, finally spoke. "What are you doing today?"

"Working on a model airplane."

"Oh."

"Why?"

"I just wondered," Bruce said.

They continued to study one another with noncommittal expressions. Charles assumed that Bruce was looking for someone to serve as his buddy, now that school was over and the long summer lay ahead.

"Do you want to come in and see my airplane?"

"Sure."

Charles opened the screen door and Bruce followed him into a tiny bedroom just inside the entrance. Next to the bed was a rickety card table covered with balsa shavings, tissue paper, glue, straight pins, paint brushes, and the skeleton of a fuselage.

"What's that stink?" Bruce said.

"Banana dope. You paint it on the paper you've glued over the ribs—like on this wing—and it pulls the paper up tight. Then you keep putting it on and putting it on until the paper is like a drum, and then you put the plane together, put on the landing gear and things, and it's ready to fly."

"How do you fly it?"

"When it's finished, I'm going to buy a motor. Free flight. Isn't it a beauty?" Charles said, and held up a picture, an artist's rendition of the finished plane, and studied it.

"Yeah." Bruce looked around the room. The bed was unmade and dozens of snapshots, as though undergoing arrangement, were spread across it. The door of the closet was open and Bruce could see, piled along its bottom, old clothes, crushed boxes, old work shoes caked with plaster (Charles's father was in the plastering business), bent coat hangers, and a torn pillow spilling feathers. There were books and magazines scattered around, and the floor was dirty. Bruce had never seen such disorder. At his house, even when they lived in the country, everybody made their beds as soon as they rose, the floors were waxed and shining, the furniture glowed, and there was a place for everything, as his mother expressed it, and everything was in its place; one asked permission before moving a piece of furniture and there was a special hassock on which to place the evening paper. Bruce knew that Charles's mother had died several years ago—he'd signed the sympathy card to Charles along with the rest of the class—and he imagined her death helped explain this mess. "Is this where you sleep?"

"Not in summer. It's too hot. Sometimes in winter I do. It's my Dad's room. He never uses it."

"Do you know my aunt, old Emma Dawson, on the other side of town?"

"Sure. What about her?"

"She wants to clean out the cats in that old barn behind her house."

"What do you mean?"

"She wants me to kill them."

"Kill them?"

"Any way I want to do it, she said. Do you want to help?"

Charles tried to suppress a surge of exhilaration that made his ribs ache. "I'm supposed to stay here and watch my sisters."

"Where are they?"

"Over on the other side of the house, I guess." It was

a task he resented and felt was unnecessary; they were six and four, self-sufficient. "Maybe my brother can watch them," Charles said. He went to the doorway and called in a loud voice, "Tim! Hey, *Tim!*"

There was a faint response from a far corner of the house.

"Come here!" Charles turned back to Bruce. "You mean she really wants them killed?"

"That's what she said."

"Did you ever kill one?"

"Sure. I choked one to death once on the farm. And another time I held a whole bag of them in the watertank until they were all drowned." Bruce grinned, showing his gapped and broken teeth, and he and Charles broke into nervous laughter and found it difficult to look at one another.

"What do you want *now?*" a plaintive voice said, and a small boy with a freckled face and freckled shoulders, wearing only a pair of bluejeans that were too big at the waist and rolled high on his shins, walked into the room. "I suppose you want—— Oooo!" he said, seeing Bruce. "A guestus! You have a guestus! Oooo!" He jumped back as though in fear, made wide eyes, and held up his hands and shook them so violently his fingers made noise knocking together.

"Come on, cut it out," Charles said. "Geez." He couldn't stand it when his brother acted this way. Unless Tim was angry (and that was an uncontrollable fury that was more like madness), he was usually bashful around people, and so quiet and retreating you seldom realized he was in the room. He even seemed shy among his own family, and when expressing an opinion he spoke in a deferential voice, with his eyes lowered, as though he couldn't bear to see either smiles or disapproval. Though he was nine, he still sat in his father's lap for hours at a time, usually with an arm around his father's neck. But lately, within the last year, every time that Charles had guests Tim went into this performance, speaking in altered voices, singing, making faces, improvising strange words and languages, doing flips that landed him on the floor on the flat of his back—anything to draw attention to himself. He bowed now to Bruce and said in an innocent voice, but with crossed eyes, "I'm Tinvalin."

Bruce turned to Charles and his invisible eyebrows drew down.

"He calls himself that," Charles explained.

"No, ho," Tim said. "I'm Toonvaloon and I'm Toon-va*loony*." The tip of his tongue appeared at the corner of his mouth and his head started jerking toward his shoulder as though he had spasms.

"What's the matter with you, anyway?" Charles said. "Cut it out."

"Nat-ur-elly, Chelly."

"Listen. Bruce and I are going out for a while. You have to watch the girls."

"No, I don't. Dad told you to watch them."

"And now I'm telling you to."

"You're not my boss."

"I am when Dad's gone."

"That's not what he says."

"*I'm* saying it."

"I'll tell him you took off and left us."

"I'll tell him how you act when he's not here."

"Try it," Tim said, and began dancing and shadow-boxing around the room, brushing his nose with his thumb, saying, "Snift! Snift! Snort-snort, snift!"

"Watch the girls! You hear?"

"Ahh-yahtata." One of his words for yes, said in imitation of a Chinese. He drew back his upper lip and bit over his lower one, exposing his front teeth, which were slightly bucked in an attractive way, and bowed again. "I hear."

"You better. And you better make sure they stay out of this room. If anything happens to my plane—"

"Oh! Precious. *Precious*."

"You're damn right."

"Wow! Big he-man rips off a swear word. Scary."

"Come on," Charles said to Bruce. "I have to put on my shoes."

Bruce followed him through a living room in worse disorder than the bedroom, through a kitchen where boxes of breakfast food and dirty dishes were sitting on a table, and down a set of steps to the basement, which was damp and chilly. Charles pulled a light chain. A high double bed with a metal frame sat next to a furnace, and there was a three-hundred-gallon oil tank in a corner beyond the furnace. The cement-block walls of the basement, once painted aqua, were stained brown and yellow and dark green from seepage, and the outlines of the stains were fringed with fuzzy deposits of lime. Two mattresses, placed side by side, lay flat on the cement floor in the middle of the room. Charles sat down on one and began pulling his shoes on over bare feet.

"Is this where you sleep?" Bruce asked.

"Yes."

"On those?"

Charles looked up and saw Bruce studying the mattresses with wide eyes. "No, no, over on the bed. These are for our tag-team matches."

"Tag-team matches?"

"Sometimes we have regular matches, one against one, but most of the time we have tag-team matches."

"Oh."

"Don't you have a television?"

"No."

"It's wrestling. In a tag-team match, you each have a partner, and if you're getting trounced and need help, you tag your partner's hand and he comes in the ring and takes over for you. We have them on Thursday nights after Boy Scouts. Do you want to come sometime?"

"Sure."

"I'm pretty good. Tim and I beat the Wilson brothers last week. I'm working on a sleeper."

"Tim wrestles?"

"Yes. He's really tough for his size. About a week ago we were playing football, and Butch Crafton got mad at me— he couldn't make any headway against our defense and I tackled him real hard once—so he jumped me and started socking me in the face, and then Tim jumped him. Crafton went home with a bloody nose."

"*Butch* Crafton?" This was a wiry, powerful classmate of theirs, much feared by most everybody their age.

"Yes. When Tim gets really mad, it's like he's crazy and you can't hold him off. It's scary. He's even beat me up a few times. Let's go," Charles said, and started up the steps.

"Hey, wait," Bruce said. "What's this?"

Charles stepped down to the dark doorway where Bruce was standing, near the foot of the stairs, and turned on a light switch. Four oil-stained steps led up to a long, wide, extensive area with black walls and a black floor, and a ceiling less than five feet high.

"Holy balls," Bruce said. "What kind of a room do you call *that*?"

"This place was a gas station once. The part above this low part was a double garage before it was remodeled, and down here was the grease pit. That old grease is baked on and won't come off. We even tried muratic acid."

"It's got a barn gutter right down the middle!"

"That's what they drained the oil and grease into, I guess. There's a big drain down at the other end that smells pretty bad."

"You'd have to be some kind of a midget or something to live in there."

"We never used it until last year. Then we made it into a shooting gallery. It's perfect."

At the far end of the room there was a cardboard backstop that reached from ceiling to floor. Two wires were strung across posts several feet in front of the backstop, and a row of paper targets, held in the jaws of clothespins, hung from each wire. Higher up, a round fruitcake can with blue target circles painted on its shiny bottom depended from a wire attached to one of the big, oil-blackened beams.

"What do you shoot with?" Bruce asked.

"A BB pistol."

"Hey, maybe we could use it on those cats, huh?"

"I doubt if it'd be powerful enough. Anyway, it's broken."

"How'd it get broke?"

"Tim got mad once and threw it on the floor. We're going to have it fixed."

"Boy," Bruce said, "you couldn't get me to go in that place for ten bucks."

"We didn't. We shot from right here."

"How'd you know if you hit anything?"

"Well, we did have to go in once and a while for a target check."

"I bet you really had to wipe your feet off afterwards, didn't you?"

Charles thought that Bruce was being very nosy and goggle-eyed, very much like a hick, with his mouth hanging open half the time, and all these questions of his were straining Charles's patience; he wanted to get at those cats.

Bruce had forgotten about the cats for the time being; he wanted to get home and tell his mother about this house.

"Let's go," Charles said, and turned off the lights. Bruce preceded Charles up the steps and as he walked into the kitchen he stopped with such suddenness that Charles bumped into him. Tim lay on his back in the middle of the floor, his head thrown back, his mouth open and the whites of his eyes visible, and his chest, along with the linoleum in his vicinity, was spattered with a thick red matter that was also trickling from his lips. The handle of a butcher knife showed above his rib cage.

"Oh, for God's sake," Charles said. "Not that again." It was about the third time Tim had used this tactic, which was instituted by Charles to frighten their sisters; the blade of the butcher knife was gripped between arm and rib cage, the red matter was ketchup. Charles walked over and prodded Tim with his toe. "Get up," he said, and Bruce, who at last realized this was another act, broke into nervous laughter.

"I thought I told you to watch the girls."

Tim lifted his head. "I can't. I'm dying. I have maybe ten seconds left." He dropped his head. "Five, four, three——"

"Get up!"

Tim jumped to his feet and tossed the knife into the sink. "Thank you," he said in a falsetto, clasping his hands together. "You've just saved my life, kind sir. How can I thank you?"

"Get over there and see what the girls are doing before I clobber you one."

"Would you care to try it?" Tim said, and began to shadowbox around. "Snift-snift, snift!" He danced to an open door, went into his fighting crouch at its edge, and began knocking the door back and forth between his fists in a noisy staccato. "The Toonvaloon rat-a-tat-tat bone-cracker, folks. Practicing up. Going to use it on the he-man, the big boss, the big scary one."

Charles walked over and slapped the back of his head. "I told you to cut it out a long time ago. And I told you to get in there and watch the girls. Now *go*." Charles turned to Bruce. "Come on," he said.

As they went through the living room, Tim danced along behind them, making his snifting sound, and just as Charles reached for the door he felt a slap, half-hearted yet impera-tive, on his back. He swung around. Tim was dancing in front of him, revolving his fists, so furious that his face was pale and there were tears in his eyes.

"Come on," Tim cried. "Come on, you chicken! Fight!"

"Don't let the girls——"

"*Come on!*"

Charles gave him a long stare of impatience and disdain and walked out the door.

THE OLD BARN was overrun with cats. There must have been thirty. After a preliminary inspection, they went to the house and Mrs. Dawson, a plump, high-strung woman with coal-black hair wound in such tight curls it seemed she was wearing a wig, gave them a bowl of scraps, saying, "I haven't put out anything for them for a week or more, so they ought to go for this like it was gold cream. It'll give you a good chance to grab some. I hate to see it come to this, but they been killing robins and getting into people's garbage and gardens and causing so much general com-plaint there's naught I can do. When I farm them out, they're back the next day, and when other people throw out the cats they don't want, *they* congregate here, and lately they been keeping up the whole neighborhood at night with their caterwauling and making new kitties. If my John was still here, things never would have come to this pass, may the Lord bless him where he lies. Remember your Uncle John, Brucie? Sure you do. All right, you boys run along." They had started toward the barn when she cried, "Now don't kill them all! I need me a few mousers."

A rock held a side door of the barn ajar. They removed it and latched the door from the inside. Until their eyes became accustomed to the darkness of the barn, the holes in its roof and sides surrounded them like distant constellations, and Charles felt as he'd felt once in a planetarium—that the Earth had shrunk to the limits of a house and he was standing at the North Pole, gigantic, and could reach out and extinguish with a fingertip, one by one, each star. When they could see well, they searched for escape exits, Bruce carrying the bowl under one arm. The building originally must have been a horse barn; there were four stalls along one side, and the other half was open, as if for parking a carriage. There was a platform loft above the stalls and an alley in front of them for throwing down hay. In a low window, Bruce discovered a broken pane and they covered it with a piece of masonite. They placed a two-by-twelve over a gap along the bottom of a pair of rolling doors.

Bruce handed the bowl of scraps to Charles and cats began leaning into his legs, running the lengths of their bodies along him, purring and meowing, arching their backs, switching him with their tails, and pawing at his pants. Bruce went into a stall filled with gardening equipment, tools, wooden boxes of junk, buckets, part of a harness and a broken singletree, and here he found and laid out a hand scythe, a baseball bat, several window-sash weights, a ball of twine, a hammer, and a fishing knife that was badly rusted and had old fish scales glittering along its blade. He cut a couple of lengths of twine about nine feet each, and made noose snares of them. These he laid aside.

He took a gunnysack and went into each of the stalls, looking in the feedboxes and mangers, and when he came across a litter of kittens, he dropped them into the sack. Mother cats were following him around, rising on their hind legs to reach the sack, showing their teeth as they meowed at him. He tied the top of the sack with twine and started out the door.

"Hey!" Charles cried. "Where do you think you're going?"

"There's an old rain barrel out behind the barn here. I'm going to put them in there and then put this on them." He turned his butt toward Charles; there was a window-sash weight in his back pocket.

"There's about half a dozen cats following you!" Charles yelled, and was amazed at his tone; it was all out of proportion to the circumstance he was pointing out and to his place in this whole matter.

Bruce reached into his shirt pocket with his forefinger and thumb and held a baby kitten up by the scruff of its neck. "They'll follow me back," he said. His face was pale. He gave a weak smile and walked out.

More cats had gathered around Charles and they were circling and milling about his legs, rising up and leaning on him with their forepaws, pressing against him with such strength and persistence he was afraid that if he moved he'd be thrown off balance and step on one. Or fall. He heard an animal sound like a shrieking hinge (an owl?) and looked up. A row of cats had gathered along the edge of the loft and they were staring down at him with extended necks, heads moving from side to side, as though readying to spring. Bruce reentered the barn with the baby kitten between his thumb and forefinger and most of the mother cats following behind. He closed the door. "The barrel's empty," he said. "I'll just leave them outside for a while till we're done in here." He went into the stall of equipment and placed the kitten in a feedbox.

"Okay," Bruce said. "Put down the food."

"*You* put it down," Charles said, and tossed the bowl to Bruce. The cats followed its flight through the air, and by the time Bruce got it to the ground they were gathered around it like spokes around a hub. The cats in the loft began leaping to the floor, one by one, like precision divers, and bounded toward the bowl, forcing their way into the mass of milling cats already there. Fights, mostly short-lived and petty, began to break out; two cats would sit back on their haunches, teeth bared, and snarl and box at one another, then drop to their feet again and crowd toward the bowl.

"Okay," Bruce said. "Where's the biggest, ugliest one of them all?"

"Right there," Charles said, and pointed out a large tiger-striped tom, leaning back on its haunches, with an enormous flattened head, a spray of needlelike whiskers, and a badly scarred nose. One of its gold eyes was clouded a pearl-gray color, either from injury or disease. "Boy," Bruce said. "He must be the granddaddy of them all. Look at those nuts on him. We better not take any chances with him. We better use the twine. He's going to be a doozie." Bruce looped the nooses together and, when the tom was boxing at a smaller cat, slipped them both over its neck and drew them tight. The tom backed away from him, shaking its head from side to side, as if to say, No, no, no, you've made a terrible mistake.

"Watch this," Bruce said. He reeled the cat toward him until it was within a few feet, and then swung it high overhead, nearly as high as the loft, and brought it down on the floor of the stall with a wallop. Hardly stunned, still held by the twines, the cat tried to claw away from Bruce. Bruce picked up the hand scythe and hit it across the neck. It turned on Bruce, laid back its ears, and spat at him with a gasping sound.

"Get it with something!" Bruce said.

"What?"

"Anything!"

Charles picked up a window-sash weight, threw it, and in his excitement missed. Bruce swung again with the scythe and caught the cat on the tail, and it let out a loud cry of anger and challenge that sent the rest of the cats bolting toward cover. One of them leaped madly against the masonite, knocking it loose, and a stream of cats— calico, tortoiseshell, spotted, tan, gray, white—began pouring out the broken window. Bruce handed Charles the twines, ran over with the baseball bat, was nearly struck in the head by a leaping cat, knocked another down in mid-air with the bat, and got the masonite back in place.

"Geez," Charles said, as the tomcat, with its back arched and its hackles up, danced on stiff legs, fighting the leash of twine. "There has to be a better way of doing this."

"How?"

"We ought to have a rifle."

"But we don't."

"How about stringing him up?"

"We could try," Bruce said, and took the twines from Charles. "You go on up in the hayloft. I'll hand you these ends."

Charles climbed up a board ladder toward the loft, feeling his heart beat so hard at the base of his throat he felt it was knocking his air out. Cats in the loft scattered from him. He walked over until he was above Bruce, and saw that some big spikes had been hammered halfway into the facer board of the loft, perhaps for hanging harness. He lay on his stomach and reached a hand down to Bruce, who was drawing the cat toward him, trying to get enough slack in the twines to hand them up, but the cat was yowling and leaping from side to side at the end of its tether, and winning in the tug-of-war. "You bastard," Bruce said, and gave a jerk, and the cat started toward Bruce as though it meant business. Bruce got the twines to Charles, Charles reeled them quickly hand over hand, suddenly feeling at their ends a tremendous, struggling, unsteady weight, and then he stood and lifted his arms high, got the twines next to a spike, pulled them to one side, and made several turns around another spike. The cat was about five feet off the floor, kicking its hind legs, springing them as though trying to leap, and clawing at the twine with its forepaws. Its scarred and battered nose was turned upward, and its undamaged gold eye, in sharp focus, fixed on Charles. He moved back out of sight. "How long?" he asked.

"That one I choked once took quite a while."

Charles came down the ladder. The cat kicked and pawed at the twine, twisting itself in circles, making moist guttural noises, and after a prolonged minute of this, with Bruce and Charles growing more and more edgy and uncomfortable, there was still no sign that it was weakening.

"I guess it doesn't work like it does with people," Bruce said.

"Now what? If we let him down, he's going to get loose."

"No he isn't," Bruce said, and picked up a three-tined pitchfork. Charles went up to the loft and lowered the cat and Bruce maneuvered a tine on either side of its neck and drove the fork into the ground so the cat was held as in a stanchion. "OK," Bruce said. "Bring the equipment." Charles moved the weights and killing tools closer, and Bruce picked up the baseball bat and struck it across the back. Charles took the hammer and hit it over the head. It fell to its side, legs pawing, and Bruce picked up the fishing knife and stabbed its throat and the knife point skidded sideways over its tough skin without penetrating. Bruce stuck the knife in the cat's ear. "Hit it!" he said.

"*What?*"

"Hit the end of the knife here. Hurry!"

"*You!*"

"I can't! I've got to hold him steady!"

Charles hit the knife with the hammer, driving it a ways into the cat's skull, and the cat let out such a piercing yowl of pain that Bruce jumped back, pulling loose the pitchfork, and the cat, with the knife protruding from its ear, came streaking past Charles. Charles stepped on the trailing twines, they pulled taut, and the cat went up in the air, its hind legs reversing with its head, and hit on its side. The knife dislodged. Bruce ran over with a window-sash weight, lifted it over his head, and brought it down hard on the cat's side. The cat stood, tottered, took off in the opposite direction, and did another flip around as the twine, still under Charles's shoe, pulled taut. Bruce picked up the pitchfork and stabbed with it like a gig. The center tine pierced the cat's abdomen and it began to growl and bark like a dog and claw at the fork as though it would climb it.

"Jesus God!" Bruce cried. "*It's got nine lives!*"

"Don't be stupid!"

"Why isn't it dead then?"

"We haven't got it in a vital place!"

"Where is one?"

Charles came over with the hammer and hit it twice at the base of the skull, then again. Its eyes clouded and closed, its tongue appeared, and its ears turned down toward earth. Blood ran from between its bared teeth and it lay still. Then it went into spasms. Bruce took the baseball bat and beat it until it was motionless. He carried it over to a stall, his face gray and set, and dropped it into a bucket. "Okay," he said, without looking at Charles. "Where's the next one?"

"That's it."

"What do you mean?"

"That's it," Charles said. "I'm quitting."

"You can't. We have to kill the rest."

"What for? Are you crazy about killing them or something?"

"Hell, no."

"Well, if you're so crazy about it, you keep doing it. I'm going home."

Charles walked out of the barn. The lawn in bright sunlight was alive with movement. Somehow, the kittens had escaped from the gunnysack, and they were crawling and tottering through the thick grass, heading toward the barn where Charles stood.

Cats poured out of the door behind him.

AT HOME, Tim was standing in the front room, wearing a black suit jacket of his father's that hung to his knees and a gray wig from an old Halloween costume. He'd found something black—cigar ash, most likely—and rubbed it over his cheeks to represent stubble. "Where's Bruce?" he asked.

"Who knows?"

"Arms for the poor," Tim said, flapping a sleeve of the coat. "Arms for the poor." He seemed reluctant to go into the act he'd prepared, and his voice lacked its usual recklessness and spirit. His face was so pale it appeared white beneath the blacking, his eyes were wide and anxious, and the saddle of freckles over his nose was glittering with points of perspiration, a sign that he was greatly agitated.

"What's wrong?"

"Nothing."

"Where are the girls?"

"Over on the other side. They're coloring."

"Why aren't you there?"

"I saw you coming. Where's Bruce?"

"Busy, I guess."

Charles walked to the bedroom doorway and saw, lying on the card table, the cause of Tim's agitation. The tissue paper for his model airplane was cut into shreds the size of confetti, and somebody had piled the shreds in a neat mound. "Dammit!" he cried, turning on Tim. "What's been going on here?"

"I did it."

"*You* did it? What the hell for?"

"I don't know."

"You don't *know!*" Charles yelled, and ran over and punched Tim in the chest.

"Don't," Tim said. The corners of his mouth pulled down, his chin creased and flattened, and tears started down his cheeks. Charles put his palms on Tim's chest and gave a hard shove and Tim went stumbling backward, trying to get his balance, and struck the wall with such force his wig flew off.

"You thought if Bruce was with me, you wouldn't get it, didn't you, damn you," Charles said, and went over and slapped his head.

"Don't," Tim said. He sat passive, his hands at his sides, and cried loudly, unable to defend or protect himself; when he believed he was at fault, he was so weak and helpless with guilt it was impossible for him to move.

"Why did you *do* it?"

"I don't know! I started cutting and I couldn't stop!"

"How can you be so stupid? That's the most stupid thing I ever heard of. You're so nutty and stupid, you ought to be sent away."

"No!" Tim said, and lay on his stomach and began rocking from side to side. "*No!*"

Charles grabbed a sleeve of the suit jacket and jerked on it, rolling Tim on his back, pulled the sleeve loose, rolled Tim again, and pulled off the jacket. "And on top of it all, you've probably gone and ruined Dad's suit coat. How can you be so stupid," Charles repeated, knowing he'd struck a sensitive spot. He walked to the couch, dropped the jacket on it, and started toward the kitchen. "Now shut up," he said. "Quit crying or you'll get some more!"

He went to the other side of the house. The girls were

sitting at a children's card table on small metal chairs, coloring the fashion illustrations from a newspaper ad. The oldest girl, Marie, a brunette whose long hair was stringy and oil-darkened, seldom washed or set, looked up at him; she had the placid face and the nearly circular eyes of the Neumiller family, only her eyes were enormous, owl-like. "I'm going to tell Dad you and Tim been fighting again."

"We haven't been."

"Sue and I heard."

"I just gave him heck. He ruined my airplane."

"*Dee*, de, *dee*, de," Susan sang, smiling and swinging a crayon like a pendulum in front of her face. "*Dee*, de, *dee*, de. You said *I'd* break it." She gave Charles a toothy grin and stuck the crayon like a hatpin in her hair, which was flaxen and cut in a style that reminded Charles of pictures of Dutch children.

"Did he watch you two at all?"

"He was with us almost all the time you were gone," Marie said. "He told us why it was more fun to color these than color books."

"Why?"

"Because nobody else in the world colors them."

"Did you see his funny clothes!" Susan said, and began giggling.

"Yes."

"Doesn't he look dumb!"

"I guess."

"Dee, de, dee, dum. Like *that*." She took the crayon from her hair and pointed at her coloring. The model's face was blackened out. Charles left the room. He couldn't find Tim anywhere on the other side of the house, and was about to go outside when he heard sounds of crying coming from upstairs. He went up the steps. The upstairs was still in the process of being remodeled. Two bedrooms had been partitioned off and some of the walls were partially covered with rock lath. Charles couldn't find Tim in either bedroom. Next to the steps there was a long wall that divided the main part of the house from the wing that had once been a double garage, a wall that was merely studs covered with insulation paper, and Charles went over to it and listened at a door there, and then opened the door onto blackness. There were no windows beyond the wall, not even ventilators to let in light, and Charles knew that it was a three-foot drop to the joists below; the ceiling of the wing was that much lower, and a floor had never been put down over it.

"Tim. Are you in there?"

"No!'

"Come on out."

"No!"

"Why?"

"I don't want to!"

An extension light was hanging from the doorknob. Charles turned it on and in its dim light he could discern the row of planks that led to a platform of old grain doors that had been laid down over the joists. Unpacked boxes from a previous move, old suitcases, and broken furniture were piled on the platform, and Tim was lying there on his stomach, his hands clasped over his head. Charles lowered himself onto the planks and walked out to him. "Come on," he said.

"I want to stay here!"

"Come on."

"This is the place I belong!"

Charles tried to lift him up, but Tim cried out and struggled, and his flesh felt so sensitive in Charles's hands that he let go. "It's just that—well, dammit, when I came home and—anyway, now somebody's going to have to go to Pekin or somewhere and get more of that paper. It's a special kind."

"I know! What's the *matter* with me?"

"I don't know."

"Why can't I do anything *right?*" Tim began rolling his head back and forth on the grain doors.

"Don't. You'll hurt yourself."

"I don't care!"

"I shouldn't have got so mad," Charles said, and sat beside him and put a hand on his shoulder.

"It wouldn't be so bad if——" Tim gasped for air. "If I —if I wasn't so *stupid!*"

"You're not. I just——"

"I am too! I don't even feel like you want me around! It feels worse than when you hit me!"

"I want you around. You're my brother."

Tim let out such a prolonged wail it seemed this injured him more than anything else.

"I do," Charles said. "You're great. You're really funny sometimes. You're my greatest friend."

Tim's crying subsided and he raised up and looked at Charles with wide eyes. "Really?" he said. His face and the upper part of his body were caked with old, blackened dust from the grain doors, and the dust was streaked with perspiration, mucous from his running nose, and tears.

"Really," Charles said.

Tim sat up, put his arms around Charles, and gripped him so tightly Charles could hardly breathe. "I feel so awful all the time," Tim said. "Inside, I feel awful."

"I'm sorry I——"

"No, no, not because of you. I like you better than anybody."

"Why then?"

"I don't know!"

"You're okay," Charles said, and patted his shoulder. One day, a short while after their mother died, Charles had come home from school and found Tim marching around the front room with his teeth bared as though in fury and his eyes crossed, and as he marched he was singing in time to his step a song he'd composed, "Oh, you cross-eyed baby with the hole in your head; oh, you cross-eyed baby, don't you wish you were dead . . ." From that time, the song had become his theme. He sang it when he was angry at the girls or when he was frustrated or hyperactive. He sang it when he was too happy to express himself. And Charles had heard him singing it in bed at night when he couldn't sleep. Charles tried to think of what their mother, who never would have inflicted this unreasonable hurt on Tim, might say to Tim if she were trying to comfort him, and he remembered waking one night to total darkness, in a house kept calm and ordered by the presence of their mother, and hearing Tim, who couldn't have been more than three, screaming in his bed across the room, and then hearing the voice of their mother. "Little one, little one, what is it?"

"A tiger's after me! He's trying to eat me up!"

"There, there, you've just had a bad dream."

"No, no, it's a *real* tiger! I know it's real. The inside of his mouth is the color of a butterfly!"

And Charles had seen, like a projection upon the blackness, the white and pink and the bright red of a lion's open mouth, and he had felt as he'd felt in the darkened barn when he and Bruce, in spite of all the wounds they had inflicted, could not make the cat relinquish its hold on life—awed and mortally afraid.

"Tim," Charles said, his voice almost a whisper. "Tim, I love you."

Two Poems

James Wright

Written in a Copy of Swift's Poems, for Wayne Burns

I promised once if I got hold of
This book, I'd send it on to you.
These are the songs that Roethke told of,
The curious music loved by few.
I think of lanes in Laracor
Where Brinsley MacNamara wrote
His lovely elegy, before
The Yahoos got the Dean by rote.

Only, when Swift-men are all gone
Back to their chosen fields by train
And the drunk Chairman snores alone,
Swift is alive in secret, Wayne:

Singing for Stella's happiest day,
Charming a charming man, John Gay,
And greeting, now their bones are lost,
Pope's beautiful, electric ghost.

Here are some songs he lived in, kept
Secret from almost everyone
And laid away, while Stella slept,
Before he slept, and died, alone.
Gently, listen, the great shade passes,
Magnificent, who still can bear,
Beyond the range of horses' asses,
Nobilities, light, light and air.

Small Frogs Killed on the Highway

STILL,
I would leap too
Into the light,
If I had the chance.
It is everything, the wet green stalk of the field
On the other side of the road.
They crouch there, too, faltering in terror,
And take strange wing. Many
Of the dead never moved, but many
Of the dead are alive forever in the split second
Auto headlights more sudden
Than their drivers know.
The drivers burrow backward into dank pools
Where nothing begets
Nothing.

Across the road, tadpoles are dancing
On the quarter thumbnail
Of the moon. They can't see,
Not yet.

Three Poems

Wm Brown

The Amoeba Aspires

SHAPELESS, save for salients
Of need and inlets
Of aversion,
Frontless, backless, sideless,
I move, but in no direction.

Whereas you, sir, hang majestically still,
A royal carcass, your muscles stiff and clear,
Full-blooded and long-boned.
Attended as though by courtiers—the scarred,
Heroic liver, the chivalrous heart, the jesting brain—
You are a man of parts.

Seeing you that way, my watery self is stirred,
My thin skin trembles in anticipation.

Aubade

ALL OVER the world,
The morning is marred by
The bellowings of
Idiot sergeants,
Man-roars whose meaning
The sad recruits
Are going to learn.

And the first light is lost
In the dismal corners
Of prison yards.
The guards' insults
And the murderous sound
Of a buzzer awaken
Murderers, thieves, and
The misconvicted.

They all rise early,
They stand in line
To wait for nothing.

With a perfect sunrise
The day begins for
The woebegone.

Questions on the Peace at Basel

BRIBES must have been taken
For this silence, and all the loud voices
Hauled away for conversations
That, one summer evening,
Carried too far.

If not, how could the citizens
Spend Sunday as they do, pale
And shirtless on the narrow
Concrete banks of the Rhine?

And how, in the little hospitals
Above them, could doctors
Worry so learnedly
About their share of Europe's
Ailing children, whose cures
Look hopeful but whose deaths
Would not be out of place?

If law here is the peace
Of hospital zones, or the surgeon's
Meticulous scrubbing up,
If the sun like a sick child
Persuades the bathers to stay
Half an hour longer,
What can the jails be for?

Finding it hard myself
In any calm to keep from shouting,
I think I know the inmates—

Baffled traveling salesmen
Who, turning in early
To strange hotels, wake up
Before morning with grippes
They can only tell about
At the top of their lungs.

The Viping Hour

William Crawford Woods

THEY KICKED THE DOOR OPEN, breaking the lock and sending splinters of raw and painted wood spinning from a corner of the smashed frame, but that was the only touch of melodrama in the whole thing, the only off-key moment in proceedings that were to be characterized by a calm and composure that Weep found progressively more frightening as the night went on.

In any case, the noise of it, the shock, the sudden rush of the plainclothesmen—there were only two, but they entered the room with the panache of an army—brought Weep halfway down almost at once, and he was appalled to realize he was moving, a robot of confusion, toward the first officer, and that his hand was floating vaguely toward the man's face, the fingers curling into an approximation of a fist as the hand traveled. The cop blocked it easily with his arm, and against the herringbone sleeve Weep's knuckles spread loosely and limply. He was close to an apology, but then his own body was moved in a semicircle, and he half-jumped and tried to pull away from the cop's grip. He thought he had probably been hit, but felt no pain. Then the quick steel circles went over his wrists, and that was it.

Weep had had experiences in which the arresting officers were so uncourtly as to cuff and cuff, so he set himself, a little sick at stomach. But he was helped up, that was all, and not too roughly. He started to get a little nervous then: things weren't impersonal. Across the room, still dark, he saw Gand and Strathmore shuffling into line by the door. Nobody was playing with guns. He began to expect the cop to bow him out of the room.

He chose to speak. "Why bug me, man? I'm not wearing

114

any craters on my forearm. The last collapsed vein I saw was in a movie about gold miners. And I don't know any names." He tried to give the cop a knowing grin, but the cop didn't know it. "This isn't the way it's done in the city."

"This isn't the city."

"So what do we do now?"

"Guess."

"I couldn't."

"Then shut up."

"I like to talk."

"We'll let you."

There was a regulation cop car outside, a small-town cop car. It looked like a taxicab. The roof light was blinking and twisting softly.

Weep stopped for a second on the steps. "Look, this is a private home. Do you have——"

"Whose?"

"Mine. My father's."

"All right, get on in back."

"Look, if you don't have——"

"Shut up. Move. *Move.*"

Gand was already in the back seat. He lifted his locked wrists to his cop. "Hey, man, take these things off, will you? I mean, what the hell do you think I am?"

"Hush."

"I mean, I'm no killer or anything, right?"

"The last kid who said that to me pulled a knife on me," the cop told him. Gand shrugged nervously. Weep and Strathmore were helped into the back seat. The door was slammed and locked from the outside and Weep's cop got in up front. "Roll down your window," he said to the cop who was driving.

Gand snickered. "You trying to avoid a contact high, man?" The cop at the wheel looked back at him through the steel grill that dropped from the roof of the car to the back of the front seat.

Weep sighed unhappily. He had used the best, real red-dirt earthmoving stuff in consequential cities, and now he was being busted in Mogenburg, South Dakota, on a wisp of third-rate gage. Anyway, it was nice to think that that was the reason why he was sitting in this cop car. "Look,

I'm sorry I hit at you," he said to his cop, "but you made me feel so . . . invaded."

"All right."

"What'll I get for that?"

"I'm not worried about that."

"I'm not worried about anything else," Weep told him. "All I've got in my possession is a half-assed high which I am rapidly losing." He halfway expected to hear the cop say, We're not interested in you, we want the big man.

"Is that all?"

"That's all, and you won't find any shit at my place, either."

"We're not looking," said the cop, almost defensively.

Yes, these cops were behaving much too well. They had not read the book about being a cop, at least not the book Weep knew. There was not enough deadness or toughness in their voices or eyes. Weep was willing to bet they had funny little guns they were terribly proficient with. And Berns-Martin holsters, or basket-woven clamshells, hollow-point bullets with heavy loads behind them. Country cops were always terribly good with guns, the way country writers are always good with biology. And these cops were dressed not too badly, though cheaply. And the one driving seemed to be enjoying the tricks of the road. They were altogether too human. Weep came all the way down. He could feel himself falling, like a thermometer, and the high flowing out of his head, like an angel. Weep the thermometer. He looked around the car. Gand and Strathmore, beside him in the back seat, were staring out the dirty windows of the cop car at the dark houses. In the front seat, the cops were sitting far apart, and Weep's cop was looking back, but only occasionally. On the sunvisor above the driver were two little pipe holsters, a brown one with a black sandblast in it, and a black one with a natural in it.

"Why mess?" Weep said again, "Why not chase a horse-thief? You don't raid monasteries, do you?"

"Marijuana is not peyote, and this isn't New Mexico, and you aren't an Indian," said Weep's cop. "Just hush, son. You haven't got anything to say I want to hear."

Weep thought a minute. The man beside him was a

murderer. At least, that was the official way to read it. That was why they were in Mogenburg, South Dakota. He nudged Strathmore and said, "Man, all they want is to meet the Lipton's salesman. That's all. O.K.?"

"No," Strathmore said.

"We've got a morals charge on you as well, Mr. Scrivner," Weep's cop said.

"What fucking kind of morals charge?" Weep demanded.

"That kind."

"I should never have come to the cruel city," Weep said. "Can I get a cigarette from you?"

"I'm afraid I don't carry your brand."

"You are a wise guy. We don't like wise guys. We are going to see if we can't maybe take some of that wiseness out of you," Weep intoned woodenly. The cop laughed, lighted a cigarette, and passed it back through the grill. Weep saw Strathmore's eyes go up and down, busy and fermenting. He wondered how much more he could safely say to him. It might be important that Strathmore believe these cops knew nothing more than what they'd seen, that all they cared about was the grass. Strathmore, Weep reflected, was a man at the very edge right now, and he might be an ill-informed man, he might not know about those fancy guns and all that country-cop speed. He relaxed a little when the car pulled into the police station parking lot. The cops took them to the desk sergeant, and they went through that, and then took them to a small bare room down the hall. Now we get the fun, Weep thought. His handcuffs, and the others', were removed. "You men can sit down there."

"I want counsel," Gand said, "I want to make a phone call."

"In time."

"Man, *this* is the time," Gand said urgently. "*The* time."

Weep's cop took off his coat. And sat down. "Mr. Scrivner, you say that address is your house? Your father's house?"

"That is correct."

"He doesn't live in it? No one does?"

"Well, I do. Now. Sort of."

"It's a summer house, or what?"

"No, an ancestral mansion. No, really, I'm not cracking wise. It is. He's going to live there when he retires."

"And the house is not currently occupied."

"By me, I said."

"And these two men."

"Yes."

"With no heat, lights, or electricity?"

"We eat in town. There's a fireplace. Anyway, we've only been here a couple days. We're going to get all that fixed up."

"You were?"

"Ah, now, look——"

"How long have you been here, Mr. Scrivner?"

"I told you. Couple days."

"Two days."

"Yeah."

"What's your occupation, Mr. Scrivner?"

"He's a sponge," Gand said.

The cop looked at him.

"We're sponges on him," Gand said nervously.

"No, they're friends," Weep said.

"Do you know why you're here?" the cop asked him.

"For blowing a little pot in the privacy of my own house," Weep said righteously.

"That could be why. There's also the business of the girl. For you."

"That's a crock of shit, lieutenant, and you know it."

"You a college man, Mr. Scrivner?"

"Yeah."

"Where?"

"Vanderbilt."

"Went to? Graduated from?"

"Went to."

The cop tapped his automatic pencil several times against his knee. He had his foot on a chair. "O.K.," he said after a minute had passed. He called a name.

"Wait a minute," Weep said. "What now?"

"We're going to let you rack in for now," the cop told him. "I'll talk to you again in the morning."

"Shall we give you our belts and watches here, or shall we have them sent?"

"Keep them. If you hang yourselves in the cold gray dawn, I'll live."

"You sound like you're destined for better things than Mogenburg, South Dakota, if I may say so without giving offense, lieutenant. May I ask what's the charge?"

"Narcotics will do for now. Stat. Rape for you."

"Who asks for I.D.'s?"

"Who hangs around high schools?"

"She told me she was a senior."

"Oh, you don't get nailed by much," the cop said. "But by enough. By enough." He motioned them to follow the man who had come in.

"What now?" Strathmore muttered.

"Oh, we escape. We file the bars and pop on our Hondas and go."

"They know," Strathmore said. Weep said nothing. He was starting to think about how badly the cops wanted Strathmore, and how they might be able to lose interest in the girl and the grass if they had him.

"They damn well know," Strathmore said again.

Gand shrugged. "Not necessarily. Why would they be going through all this mysterious bullshit if they knew?"

"Ah, the devious workings of the totalitarian mind."

They were walking down a flight of metal stairs, a cop behind them. He herded them through a door at the foot of the stairs. It was not the general tank, but a small room with three cots and no windows and a bucket. Two of the cots were bolted against the wall. The third had been dragged in. Its tracks lay in the dust on the floor. "Isn't that cute?" Weep spat disgustedly into the bucket. "They know we want to be together."

"I'm surprised they don't have the mike slung from the ceiling on the assumption we'd mistake it for a light cord," Gand said. He raised his voice. "——and golly gee, fellows, if we don't get out of here quick, we'll miss our contact for that seven million dollars' worth of uncut horse Mr. Big has for us!"

Strathmore, who was looking into the bucket, cursed and

moved away. "You know," he said, "when I had that shitty file clerk job, I used to kill time by composing enormous symphonies in my head. The damn things would last the full eight-mothering-hour day."

Weep had sat down on a cot and was jamming his right hand deep into his pants pocket. When he withdrew it, there were tiny scales of greenish leaf on his fingertips.

"Jesus Christ, man," Gand said. "Get rid of that shit!"

"Don't sweat it. I'm not gonna smoke it. I'm gonna secrete it on my person, if you follow me."

"Stop being stupid," Strathmore told him. "Dump that shit in the toilet bucket."

"You dump it," Weep said, and he tensed. Strathmore came over fast, wrestled the tiny packet from Weep's pocket, and dumped it. Weep, who had been knocked over, got up, red. There was a cot between them. Gand watched. Weep went onto the cot, on his knees, and tried to get at Strathmore from that clumsy position, and Strathmore clipped him swiftly behind the neck, and stepped back as Weep fell forward onto the cot and kept going right on over, rolled onto the floor, and when Weep was on the floor, Strathmore put his foot on the back of Weep's neck and pushed one time. Then he stepped back.

Weep rolled, spat, and got up rockily. He started for Strathmore again.

"Ah, drop it," Gand said. But he did not move between them.

Strathmore kept Weep at arm's length for a minute or so. But then Weep got inside and doubled him over. He stayed over and butted Weep in the stomach and went over with him onto a cot and then on over and onto the floor again. Weep got up first and used his feet. Strathmore couldn't, finally, get away from them, so he gave up and went out, and Weep used his feet for several seconds, and then went over and sat down with a grunt on his cot.

"You're such a buddy," Gand said to him.

Weep iced his eyes. "Man backs his play. Man comes into the Long Branch lookin' for me, ah figger to have mine loose in the leather."

"Such a smiling, wise, friendly, funny guy."

"O.K., sponge."

"I've got my pride."

"O.K."

"Did you break anything?"

"I don't think so."

Gand let his head sink into his hands. "It was a stupid thing to do. Why get him all psyched out? There's enough trouble."

"We don't know what we're talking about, do we?"

"We know who the man wants. And it's not me. And it's not you."

"It's me, all right," Weep said, "and it's you. Don't kid yourself. That little matter of the lady is not just talk. And you know damn well we're in it with Strathmore, up to here."

"Yeah. But they *want* him. If we——"

"Shut up. I didn't kick him that hard."

Gand leaned forward and looked at the man on the floor. "He's out. But seriously, man, these officials are making me no end of nervous. They're much too damn cool, calm, and collected. They may have a lot more going for them than we think."

" '. . . and oft 'tis seen, the wicked prize itself . . .' "

Strathmore moved slowly on the floor, then sat up, bending from the waist with telling muscularity. "Scriv," he said slowly, "you're almost as good as streetbred. But you don't know, you still don't know, how to go to town, really go to town, when you've got all the cards." He pulled himself onto a cot, his face already empurpled, mouth open, the pink wad of his tongue gently testing itself between the faces of his teeth.

"Ah, chrissake," Weep grinned disarmingly, pulling his smile from his clean college-kid myth heritage. "Why the hell would I want to go to town on you, masked man? You were pushy, I was stupid. Let's forget it."

"Yes, yes, make common cause, baby," Gand muttered. "We got griefs."

The door of their room, their cell, pushed open. "Scrivner."

"I thought the fun and games were being held over," Weep protested. But he looked at the others and let his grin go crooked under the nose. "Gentlemen, it's just like

I never knew you. Either of you. O.K.?" He went out into the clean dead fishlight of the corridor. "Back upstairs?"

"Back upstairs." It was the cop who had grilled them (no, not at all: gently baked them) thirty minutes earlier.

In the bare room, Weep carefully took his old seat. He tried to keep his eyes still, but he knew the lieutenant was watching them walk.

"Cigarette?"

"Act two already, huh?"

"Mr. Scrivner, I won't waste your time. Don't waste mine. Even in Mogenburg, South Dakota, we don't summon a grand jury every time some perpetual adolescent decides to take tea and see. You know what we want. You know we've got him. All you can do is help simplify the paperwork. You do that, and you and your other buddy can walk out of here and establish a center for psychedelic research at the corner of First and Front for all I give a damn."

"My God and my Jesus," Weep said thoughtfully. "New York's finest will be grateful. Of course, it couldn't have been an accident."

"We'll settle for manslaughter."

"We?"

The lieutenant smiled. "Yeah, we. We'll settle for manslaughter."

"But you'll go for first degree."

"Yes."

"And you'll get it."

"——yes."

Weep sighed. "Lieutenant, I can't help you."

"That business about the girl. The more I think about it, the clearer it seems to me she looked at least thirty. And the whole town knows she goes down for bubble gum."

"Lieutenant," said Weep carefully, "your whole operation up to this point has been simply rancid with subtlety. Why ruin a perfectly good one?"

"You sure?"

"I'd really like to help you. But yeah, I'm sure."

"Look at it this way, then. The more I think about it,

the clearer it seems to me that that girl was a pink-cheeked virgin with one foot in the cradle. You have no idea how us simple country folk hate despoilers."

The cop had thrown his cigarettes on the scarred steel desk. Two or three poked slender fingers from the wrinkled pack, and Weep now leaned forward and pulled one free. He stood. "Lieutenant, let me sleep on it."

"Be my guest. Light?"

"No, thanks."

"No?"

"I'm saving it for my mother. I never smoke tobacco. Have you seen the pictures of what it does to your lungs?"

"Horrible."

"I suppose you'd like me to send Gand on up."

"Might as well."

"He won't do you any good. He's even more noble than I am."

"Let's just see. You have no idea how us simple country folk hate and despise potheads."

"Potheads!" Weep was suddenly swamped with anger. "Look, why not just get your best man and talk to him in that special way you fucking cops learned from all those neat movies about the Gestapo?"

"Because that isn't even necessary," the lieutenant said, without rancor. "Now get going. And send Gand up."

"No, man, I think I'll just make a run for it as soon as I'm in the hall. Everybody else has to be asleep at this ungodly hour, and that winner at the desk didn't look like he could stop a half-trained flea with a howitzer."

"He doesn't look like he could stop a cough with a Kleenex. But if you run, go fast."

Weep grinned. He went into the corridor and, with a cop behind him, through the bad dead levels of timeless light to the stairs and the cell. The cop unlocked the door and Weep went into the little room. "Mr. Gand, the headmaster will see you now. And if you're not ready to tell him where you got those filthy pictures, you can plan on having your weekend privileges suspended for the rest of the semester."

Strathmore said, "How about you, Weep?"

"Baby, I've had mine suspended for the year." But he was nervous.

"I go up now?" Gand asked.

"Yeah. And don't sweat it. These sadsack heat have us confused with some other cases."

Gand used the bucket and left.

"Is that true?" Strathmore asked a minute later, breaking a silence which was beginning to have a very real weight.

"Hell, yes. They're shooting fish in an empty barrel. Couple phone calls in the morning, and we give 'em the bird."

"You make me feel all warm inside. I suppose that now they've asked you to fill dossiers on Bruce and me, and now they're asking him to fill 'em on me and you, they'll ask me about you and him."

"Yeah, I guess so."

"What if they don't?"

"You'll have a nervous night."

"*You'll* have a very nervous night."

"Look, man, ease up. I'm telling you these people are just killing time. Pity them. I mean, if you were a cop in this town, with nothing to do but lay traps for the City Council sodomists and shoo pigeons off the statue of General Mogen, wouldn't you look for laughs wherever you could find them? Be charitable."

"I hope you haven't been too charitable."

Gand came in sometime later. Strathmore and Weep knew, to the minute, how long he had been gone. It was an odd time: too long to have said nothing, too short to have said enough. Gand shriveled up on his rack, wordlessly, and began to dupe the sleep that lurked in the shadows of the naked lightbulb, which was glowing faintly in its wire mesh cage. And Weep suddenly felt very safe, because the burden of their drama had passed from him to Gand, who had been the latest and the last to parley with the opposition.

Strathmore said at last, "They must be pretty sure." He was drawing steel for his voice from some bank of nerve in which he had clearly never made a deposit.

"Sleep," said Gand wearily. "Sleep, you cowboys. You schmucks."

In the morning, the atmosphere had not changed, but was rather fulfilled, realized, as though armies of angel messengers had come by in the night, with dreams and modifications. They took Strathmore after all, and pushed him into another police car, one that had steel shutters in a box in the back, and cuffed him to one of the frames, hands crossed, so that his fingers pushed the glass where they could touch it, and made flesh spots and rims of callus and horn. And when they came to take Strathmore from the cell, Weep said sententiously to the lieutenant, "Oh, I know you, you're a *bad* charity, you only show pity to those who show woe." He did not look at Strathmore, nor Strathmore at him, nor at Gand. But when the cops had moved out into the corridor with their prisoner, Weep said to Gand:

"——and what did you do in the war, Daddy?"

"Son, I was in the infantry."

"Ooooo, I'll bet you were brave, huh?"

"Son, I was scared the whole time."

Seeing Red

Irving Feldman

1

Twice a week, fantastic and compelled,
beyond the half-drawn window shade, voice
ablaze, she yanked a suitcase off the bed,
unloosed the death ray of her drop-dead stare
and parting gusts of her furious red head.
"You'll see!" she screamed and slammed the door.
So?

So nothing. She crept back in
and cried and fell asleep and slept.
A lion was on the landing,
a mouse was in the marrow inching.
Cornered, she poked at the burning eyes,
she spat at them, she hissed.
Fury and Misery.
The lion leaped and tore her thighs,
mice were gnawing in her feet.
A restless girl, a rotten period.

"Feh! She talks like a mocky."
                                    So, my sisters
while we lie and peep across the airshaft.
Then I, like the summer dawn's ambitious sun,
—eager to shine and burning to please—pink
with preference, ignite my gift for scorn
in the vacancy of understanding.
(Let them be praised! these redhaired sisters
who taught the senses' prosperous bride
the famine arts of transcendence:
bitching, snobbery, and condescension.
Their smell, the pale juvenile nighties,
the bloodlettings of their reddened fingernails
on passionate mornings—damp and idleness
and tempers and kicking in the tangled sheet
—brought me to a woman's country
of warmth, disorder, and cruelty,
biting envies and a smoldering shame,
so that I don't know yet if my mockery
is defending a privilege or a pain.)
My act is idiot approval that stings
her sleep. *I* am the little devil spurred
to spank those cheeks and rout her from bed,
nerves afire with sarcasm and applause.

2

One day, I think, driven as ever,
she got to the door and didn't stop,
set off with her squat delirious suitcase
to wow America, or marry
—like an absentminded salesman,
his dirty wash in the sample case,
and they want it! they buy!

Who needs talent, with such despair?
What else is America for!
Bad news, bad breath, bad manners,
the grievous suitcase marches on,
prophesying from every corner.
"Betrayal!" it screams
and snaps itself shut.
What a start in life!
those scraps of rumpled underwear and clothes,
sloppy habits, bad teeth, a roaring tongue,
a crummy job and worse marriage.

3

Rising beyond the pane,
red and pale, feverish, gaunt,
burnt crust but raw dough,
you grip your satchel
and leap through the window into
the middle of the Great Depression,
your eyes endowed with total misunderstanding.

4

Would it be too fatuous of me
and too late, too squeamish, too phoney,
too positively American,
touching three small fingers to my brim,
to say across thirty feet of foul airshaft,
thirty years of life, "Help you with your bags, Red?"

The Concept of Character in Fiction

William H. Gass

I HAVE NEVER found a handbook on the art of fiction or the stage, nor can I imagine finding one, that did not contain a chapter on the creation of character, a skill whose mastery, the author of each manual insists, secures for one the inner secrets of these arts: not, mind you, an easy thing; rather, as difficult as the whole art itself, since, in a way, it *is* the whole art: to fasten in the memory of the reader, like a living presence, some bright human image. All well and good to paint a landscape, evoke a feeling, set a tempest loose, but not quite good enough to nail an author to his immortality if scheming Clarence, fat, foul-trousered Harry, or sweetly terraced Priss do not emerge from the land they huff and rage and eat in fully furnished out by Being; enough alive, indeed, to eat and huff in ours—dear God! more alive than that—sufficiently enlarged by genius that they threaten to eat up and huff down everything in sight.

Talk about literature, when it is truly talk about something going on in the pages, if it is not about ideas is generally about the people in it, and ranges from those cries of wonder, horror, pleasure, or surprise, so readily drawn from the innocently minded, to the annotated stammers of the most erudite and nervous critics. But it is all the same. Great character is the most obvious single mark of great literature. The rude, the vulgar, may see in Alyosha nothing more than the image of a modest, God-loving youth; the scholar may perceive through this demeanor a symbolic form; but the Alyosha of the untutored is somehow more real and present to him than the youth on his street whom he's known since childhood, loving of his God and modest too, equally tried, fully as patient; for in some way Alyosha's visionary figure will take lodging in him, make a model for him, so to reach, without the scholar's inflationary gifts, general form and universal height; whereas the neighbor may merely move away, take cold, and forget to write. Even the most careful student will admit that fiction's fruit survives its handling and continues growing off the tree. A great character has an endless interest; its fascination never wanes. Indeed it is a commonplace to say so. Hamlet. Ahab. Julien Sorel. Madame Bovary. There is no end to their tragedy. Great literature is great because its characters are great, and characters are great when they are memorable. A simple formula. The Danish ghost cries to remember him, and obediently—for we are gullible and superstitious clots—we do.

It hasn't always been a commonplace. Aristotle regarded character as a servant of dramatic action, and there have been an endless succession of opinions about the value and function of characters since—all dreary—but the important thing to be noted about nearly every one of them is that whatever else profound and wonderful these theories have to say about the world and its personalities, characters are clearly conceived as living outside language. Just as the movie star deserts herself to put on some press agent's more alluring fictional persona, the hero of a story sets out from his own landscape for the same land of romance the star reached by stepping there from life. These people—Huckleberry Finn, the Snopes, Prince Myshkin, Pickwick, Molly Bloom—seem to have come to the words of their novels like a visitor to town . . . and later they leave on the arm of the reader, bound, I suspect, for a shabbier hotel, and dubious entertainments.

However, Aristotle's remark was a recommendation. Characters ought to exist for the sake of the action, he thought, though he knew they often did not, and those who nowadays say that given a sufficiently powerful and significant plot the characters will be dominated by it are simply answered by asking them to imagine the plot of *Moby Dick* in the hands of Henry James, or that of *Sanctuary* done into Austen. And if you can persuade them to try (you will have no success), you may then ask how the heroes and the heroines come out. The same disastrous exercise can be given those who believe that traits make character like definitions do a dictionary. Take any set of traits you like and let Balzac or Joyce, Stendhal or Beckett, loose in a single paragraph to use them. Give your fictional creatures qualities, psychologies, actions, manners, moods; present them from without or from within; let economics matter, breeding, custom, history; let spirit wet them like a hose: all methods work, and none do. The nature of the novel will not be understood at all until this is: *from any given body of fictional text, nothing necessarily follows, and anything plausibly may.* Authors are gods—a little tinny sometimes but omnipotent no matter what, and plausible on top of that, if they can manage it.

THOUGH THE HANDBOOKS try to tell us how to create characters, they carefully never tell us we are making images, illusions, imitations. Gatsby is not an imitation, for there is nothing he imitates. Actually, if he were a copy, an illusion, sort of shade or shadow, he would not be called a character at all. He must be unique, entirely himself, as if he had a self to be. He is required, in fact, to act *in character,* like a cat in a sack. No, theories of character are not absurd in the way representational theories are; they are absurd in a grander way, for the belief in Hamlet (which audiences often seem to have) is like the belief in God—incomprehensible to reason—and one is inclined to seek a motive: some deep fear or emotional need.

There are too many motives. We pay heed so easily. We are so pathetically eager for this other life, for the sounds of distant cities and the sea; we long, apparently, to pit ourselves against some trying wind, to follow the fortunes of a ship hard beset, to face up to murder and fornication, and the somber results of anger and love; oh, yes, to face up—*in books* . . . when on our own we scarcely breathe. The tragic view of life, for instance, in Shakespeare or in Schopenhauer, Unamuno, Sartre, or Sophocles, is not one jot as pure and penetratingly tragic as a pillow stuffed with Jewish hair, and if we want to touch life where it burns, though life is what we are even now awash with—futilely, stupidly drawing in—we ought not to back off from these other artifacts (wars, pogroms, poverty: men make them, too). But of course we do, and cue up patiently instead to see Prince Hamlet moon, watch him thrust his sword through a curtain, fold it once again into Polonius, that foolish old garrulous proper noun. The so-called life one finds in novels, the worst and best of them, is nothing like actual life at all, and cannot be; it is not more real, or thrilling, or authentic; it is not truer, more complex, or pure, and its people have less spontaneity, are less intricate, less free, less full.

It is not a single cowardice that drives us into fiction's fantasies. We often fear that literature is a game we can't afford to play—the product of idleness and immoral ease. In the grip of that feeling it isn't life we pursue, but the point and purpose of life—its facility, its use. So Sorel is either a man it is amusing to gossip about, to see in our friends, to puppet around in our dreams, to serve as our more able and more interesting surrogate in further fanciful adventures; or Sorel is a theoretical type, scientifically profound, representing a deep human strain, and the writing of *The Red and the Black* constitutes an advance in the science of—what would you like?—sociology?

BEFORE RECITING a few helpless arguments, let me suggest, in concluding this polemical section, just how absurd these views are which think of fiction as a mirror or a window onto life—as actually creative of living creatures—for really one's only weapon against Tertullians is ridicule.

There is a painting by Picasso which depicts a pitcher, candle, blue enamel pot. They are sitting, unadorned, upon the barest table. Would we wonder what was cooking in that pot? Is it beans, perhaps, or carrots, a marmite? The orange of the carrot is a perfect complement to the blue of the pot, and the genius of Picasso, neglecting nothing, has surely placed, behind that blue, invisible disks of dusky orange, which, in addition, subtly enrich the table's velvet brown. Doesn't that seem reasonable? Now I see that it must be beans, for above the pot—you can barely see them—are quaking lines of steam, just the lines we associate with boiling beans . . . or is it blanching pods? Scholarly research, supported by a great foundation, will discover that exactly such a pot was used to cook cassoulet in the kitchens of Charles the Fat . . . or was it Charles the Bald? There's a dissertation in that. And this explains the dripping candle standing by the pot. (Is it dripping? no? a pity. Let's get on.) For isn't Charles the Fat himself that candle? Oh, no, he's not! Blows are struck. Reputations made and ruined. Someone will see eventually that the pot is standing on a table, not a stove. But the pot has just come from the stove, it will be pointed out. Has not Picasso caught that vital moment of transition? The pot is too hot. The brown is burning. Oh, not *this* table, which has been coated with resistant plastic. Singular genius—blessed man—he thinks of everything.

Here you have half the history of our criticism in the novel. Entire books have been written about the characters in Dickens, Trollope, Tolstoi, Faulkner. But why not? Entire books have been written about God, his cohorts, and the fallen angels.

II

DESCARTES, examining a piece of beeswax fresh from the hive, brought it near a flame and observed all of its sensible qualities change. He wondered why he should believe that wax remained. His sensations lent him nothing he could fasten his judgment firmly to. Couldn't he give that puddle in his hand another name? He might have added that the sleights of the mountebanks did not bewilder him. Somehow he knew milady's hankie didn't disappear in a fist to emerge as a rose. It occurred to Descartes then that perhaps his imagination was the unifying faculty. But the wax was capable of an infinite number of spills, reaching every stage of relaxation, and he was unable, he writes in what is now a brilliant phrase, "to compass this infinity by imagination." How then? Some higher, finer capacity was required. His knowledge of the wax, soft or hard, sweet or flat, became an intuition of the mind.

Like so many philosophical arguments, this one was erected upside down, and consequently is a bit unsteady on its head. How, I'd rather ask, from the idea of wax, can we predict and picture just this sticky mess? What do we see when we peer through a glass of words?

If we ask this question of Hume, he will give us, as usual, a brilliantly reasonable, and entirely wrong, answer —out of the habit empiricists have, I suppose, of never inspecting their experience. Nothing is more free than the imagination of man, he says; "it can feign a train of events with all the appearance of reality. . . ." *With all the appearance of reality.* . . . Then we might suppose that it's my imagination which allows me to descend from a writer's words, like a god through the clouds, and basket down on sweet Belinda's belly at the moment of her maximum response (or less excitingly, to picture upon the palm in my mind a slowly sprawling blob of molten wax).

To imagine so vividly is either to be drunk, asleep, or mad. Such images are out of our control and often terrifying. If we could feign with *every* appearance of reality, we would not wish to feign *Nostromo*, or even *Pride and Prejudice*. Of course, the imagination cannot give us every appearance of reality, and just as well, but perhaps it can give us every appearance of a *faded* reality: the shadow of Belinda's body on the bed (so far has this theory fallen through the space of a sentence!), an image seen the way I see this print and paper now, though with the mind's disocular eye. Or, as Gilbert Ryle writes:

Sometimes, when someone mentions a blacksmith's forge, I find myself instantaneously back in my childhood, visiting a local smithy. I can vividly "see" the glowing red horseshoe on the anvil, fairly vividly "hear" the hammer ringing on the shoe and less vividly "smell" the singed hoof. How should we describe this "smelling in the mind's nose"?

Certainly not by explaining that there is a smell in me, a shadow of a smell, a picture of a smell, an image, and putting to my noseless spirit the task of smelling it. Not as a bruise to its blow, as Ryle says, are our imaginings related to our experience. Yet Hume sometimes supposes that imagination works like madness. If it can give to fiction all the appearance of reality, how is one to know what to believe when an author's words, stirring in us like life, managing our minds with the efficiency of reality, throw Anna Karenina under the train's wheels before our eyes?

Here is the whole thing in a single passage:

> The imagination has the command over all its ideas and can join and mix and vary them in all the ways possible. It may conceive fictitious objects with all the circumstances of place and time. It may set them in a manner before our eyes, in their true colors, just as they might have existed. But as it is impossible that this faculty of imagination can ever, of itself, reach belief, it is evident that belief consists not in the peculiar nature or order of ideas, but in the manner of their conception and in their feeling to the mind. (Hume, *An Enquiry Concerning Human Understanding*)

The name of this feeling is belief, and I am given it by the greater intensity and steadiness with which actual impressions occupy me—a narrow difference, one only of degree. Don't mystery stories make us lock our doors?

But I should suppose that "seeing things" through novels did not involve succumbing to a drunken frenzy, finding animals in walls or naked ladies draped on desert rocks like some long celibate St. Anthony.

WE DO VISUALIZE, I suppose. Where did I leave my gloves? And then I ransack a room in my mind until I find them. But the room I ransack is abstract—a simple schema. I leave out the drapes and the carpet, and I think of the room as a set of likely glove locations. The proportion of words which we can visualize is small, but quite apart from that, another barrier to the belief that vivid imagining is the secret of a character's power is the fact that when we watch the pictures which a writer's words have directed us to make, we miss their meaning, for the point is *never* the picture. It also takes concentration, visualization does—takes slowing down; and this alone is enough to rule it out of novels which are never waiting, always flowing on.

> Instantly Hugh's shack began to take form in her mind. But it was not a shack—it was a home! It stood, on wide-girthed strong legs of pine, between the forest of pine and high, high waving alders and tall slim birches, and the sea. There was the narrow path that wound down through the forest from the shore, with salmonberries and thimbleberries and wild blackberry bushes that on bright winter nights of frost reflected a million moons; behind the house was a dogwood tree that bloomed twice in the year with white stars. Daffodils and snow-drops grew in the little garden. (Lowry, *Under the Volcano*)

And so forth. Do you have all that? the salmonberries and the thimbleberries? I'm afraid you'll be all day about it. One reason is that our imaginings are mostly imprecise. They are vague and general. Even when colored, they're gray.

> A hare vaguely perceived is nevertheless a specific hare. But a hare which is the object of a vague image is a vague hare. (Sartre, *Psychology of Imagination*)

Consequently, writing which carefully defines its object, however visual its terms, sets the visual successfully aside. It does, that is, if what we see inside us are misty visual schema. But

> Suppose that I have an image of a head that is non-specific about baldness, is this not rather queer? For presumably this head must be neither bald nor not bald nor even a half-way house with just a few hairs. (J. M. Shorter, "Imagination," *Mind*, LXI)

Enter Mr. Cashmore, who is a character in *The Awkward Age*.

> Mr. Cashmore, who would have been very red-headed if he had not been very bald, showed a single eye-glass

and a long upper lip; he was large and jaunty, with little petulant movements and intense ejaculations that were not in the line of his type.

We can imagine any number of other sentences about Mr. Cashmore added to this one. Now the question is: What is Mr. Cashmore? Here is the answer I shall give: Mr. Cashmore is (1) a noise, (2) a proper name, (3) a complex system of ideas, (4) a controlling conception, (5) an instrument of verbal organization, (6) a pretended mode of referring, and (7) a source of verbal energy. But Mr. Cashmore is not a person. He is not an object of perception, and nothing whatever that is appropriate to persons can be correctly said of him. There is no path from idea to sense (this is Descartes' argument in reverse), and no amount of careful elaboration of Mr. Cashmore's single eyeglass, his upper lip, or jauntiness is going to enable us to *see* him. How many little petulant movements are there? Certainly as many as the shapes which may be taken by soft wax. If we follow Hume, we think we picture things through language because we substitute, on cue, particular visual memories of our own, and the more precisely language defines its object, the less likely we are to find a snapshot in our book to fit it. This is not a harmless error either, but a vulgar and pernicious one. Our visualizations interfere with Mr. Cashmore's development, for if we think of him as someone we have met, we must give him qualities his author hasn't yet, and we may stubbornly, or through simple lack of attention, retain these later, though they've been explicitly debarred. "On your imaginary forces work," *Henry V's* Prologuer begs. "Piece out our imperfections with your thoughts. . . . Think, when we talk of horses, that you see them/ Printing their proud hoofs i' th' receiving earth," and then the audience (and the similarly situated novel reader) is praised for having done so; but this is worse than the self-congratulating pap which periodically flows from the bosom of the "creative" critic, because these generous additions destroy the work as certainly as "touching up" and "painting over." The unspoken word is often eloquent.

Well, I finally met Mr. Mulholland.

Oh, what's he like?
He has large thumbs.

CHARACTERS IN FICTION are mostly empty canvas. I have known many who have passed through their stories without noses, or heads to hold them; others have lacked bodies altogether, exercised no natural functions, possessed some thoughts, a few emotions, but no psychologies, and apparently made love without the necessary organs. The true principle is direct enough: Mr. Cashmore has what he's been given; he also *has* what he *hasn't*, just as strongly. Mr. Cashmore, in fact, has been cruelly scalped.

Now, is there a nose to this Mr. Cashmore? Let's suppose it—but then, of what sort? We're not told. He is an eyeglass without eyes, he has no neck or chin, his ears are unexplored. "Large"—how indefinite a word. But would it have been better to have written "sixteen stone"? Not at all, nor do we know how this weight is disposed. If it is impossible to picture Mr. Cashmore, however carefully we draw him, will it be easier to limn his soul? Or perhaps we may imagine that this sentence describes not Mr. Cashmore, out or in, but his impression—what sort of dent he makes in his surroundings. He gives the impression of a man who would have been redheaded if he hadn't been bald. Very well. What impression, exactly, is that? Will it do to think of Mr. Cashmore as a man with red eyebrows and a red fringe above his ears, but otherwise without hair? That would rephrase Mr. Cashmore, and rephrase him badly. The description of Mr. Cashmore stands as James wrote it, even if Mr. Cashmore hasn't a hair on his body.

As a set of sensations Mr. Cashmore is simply impossible; as an idea he is admirably pungent and precise.

Similarly, it is not at all correct to infer that because Mr. Mulholland has thumbs, he has hands, arms, torso, self. That inference destroys the metaphor (a pure synechdoche), since his thumbs are all he seems to be. Mr. Mulholland is monumentally clumsy, but if you fill him in behind his thumbs, clumsiness will not ensue.

So sometimes, then, we are required to take away what we've been given, as in the case of Mr. Cashmore's red hair;

sometimes it's important to hold fast to what we've got and resist any inclination we may have to elaborate, as in the case of Mr. Mulholland, who I said had thumbs; and sometimes we must put our minds to the stretch, bridging the distances between concepts with other concepts, as in the two examples which follow; or we may be called upon to do all these things at once, as in what I promise will be my final misuse of poor Mulholland.

Well, I finally met Mr. Mulholland.
Oh, what's he like?
A silver thimble.

I saw Mr. Mulholland today.
Oh, what was he doing?
Walking his thumbs.

Mr. Mulholland's face had
a watchful look. Although
its features had not yet arrived,
they were momentarily expected.

To summarize, so far:

1. Only a few of the words which a writer normally uses to create a character can be "imaged" in any sense.

2. To the extent these images are faded sensations which we've once had, they fill in, particularize, and falsify the author's account.

3. To the degree these images are as vivid and as lively as reality is, they will very often be unpleasant, and certainly can't be "feigned." Then words would act like a mind-expanding drug.

4. To the degree these images are general schema, indistinct and vague, the great reality characters are supposed to have become less plausible, and precise writing (so often admired) will interfere with their formation.

5. Constructing images of any kind takes time, slows the flow of the work; nor can imaging keep up, in complexity, with the incredibly intricate conceptual systems which may be spun like a spiderweb in a single sentence.

6. We tend to pay attention to our pictures, and lose sight of the meaning. The novelist's words are not notes which he is begging the reader to play, as if his novel

needed something more done to it in order to leap into existence.

WORDS in daily life are signposts, handles, keys. They express, instruct, command, inform, exhort—in short, they serve; and it is difficult to think of our servants as kings. But among real things words win the gold medals for Being. Ortega y Gasset asks us to imagine we are looking through a window at a garden.

> The clearer the glass is, the less (of the glass) we will see. But then making an effort we may withdraw attention from the garden; and by retracting the ocular ray, we may fixate it upon the glass. Then the garden will disappear in our eyes and we will see instead only some confused masses of color which seem to stick to the glass. Consequently to see the garden and to see the glass in the window-pane are two incompatible operations. . . . Likewise he who in the work of art aims to be moved by the fate of John and Mary, or of Tristan and Iseult, and readjusts to them his spiritual perception will not be able to see the work of art. . . . Now the majority of people are unable to adjust their attention to the glass and the transparency which is the work of art; instead they penetrate through it to passionately wallow in the human reality which the work of art refers to. If they are invited to let loose their prey and fix their attention upon the work of art itself, they will say they see nothing in it, because, indeed, they see no human realities there, but only artistic transparencies, pure essences. (*The Dehumanization of Art*)

Ortega seems to believe, however, that words are windows through which something can be seen, and I have argued that words are opaque, as opaque as my garden gloves and trowel, objects which, nevertheless, may vividly remind me of spring, earth, and roses. Or Uncle Harry, Africa, the tsestse fly, and love-sick elephants.

On the other side of a novel lies the void. Think, for instance, of a striding statue; imagine the purposeful inclination of the torso, the alert and penetrating gaze of the head, the outstretched arm and pointing finger; everything would appear to direct us toward some goal in front of it. Yet our eye travels only to the finger's end, and not beyond. Though pointing, the finger bids us stay instead, and we journey slowly back along the tension of the arm. In our hearts we know what actually surrounds that statue. The same surrounds every other work of art: empty space and silence.

III

A CHARACTER, first of all, is the noise of his name, and all the sounds and rhythms that proceed from him. We pass most things in novels as we pass things on a train. The words flow by like the scenery. All is change. But there are some points in a narrative which remain relatively fixed; we may depart from them, but soon we return, as music returns to its theme. Characters are those primary substances to which everything else is attached. Hotels, dresses, conversations, sausage, feelings, gestures, snowy evenings, faces—each may fade as fast as we read of them. Yet the language of the novel will eddy about a certain incident or name, as Melville's always circles back to Ahab and his wedding with the white whale. Mountains are characters in Malcolm Lowry's *Under the Volcano*, so is a ravine, a movie, mescal, or a boxing poster. A symbol like the cross can be a character. An idea or a situation (the anarchist in *The Secret Agent*, bomb ready in his pocket), or a particular event, an obsessive thought, a decision (Zeno's, for instance, to quit smoking), a passion, a memory, the weather—anything, indeed, which serves as a fixed point, like a stone in a stream or that soap in Bloom's pocket, functions as a character. Character, in this sense, is a matter of degree, for the language of the novel may loop back seldom, often, or incessantly. But the idea that characters are like primary substances has to be taken in a double way, because if any thing becomes a character simply to the degree the words of the novel qualify it, it also loses some of its substance, some of its primacy, to the extent that it, in turn, qualifies something else. In a perfectly organized novel, every word would ultimately qualify one thing, like the God of the metaphysician, at once the subject and the body of the whole. Normally, characters are fictional human beings, and thus are given proper names. In such cases, to create a character is to give meaning to an unknown *X*; it is *absolutely* to *define*; and since nothing in life corresponds to these *X*'s, their reality is borne by their name. They *are*, where it *is*.

Most of the words the novelist uses have their meanings already formed. Proper names do not, except in a tangential way. It's true that Mr. Mulholland could not be Mr. Mull, and Mr. Cashmore must bear, as best he can, the curse of his wealth forever, along with his desire for gain. Character has a special excitement for a writer (apart from its organizing value) because it offers him a chance to give fresh meaning to new words. A proper name begins as a blank, like a wall or a canvas, upon which one might paint a meaning, perhaps as turbulent and mysterious, as treacherous and vast, as Moby Dick's, perhaps as delicate, scrupulous, and sensitive as that of Fleda Vetch.

CANNOT PAUSE here over the subject of rhythm and sound, though they are the heartbeat of writing, of prose no less than poetry.

> Their friend, Mr. Grant-Jackson, a highly preponderant pushing person, great in discussion and arrangement, abrupt in overture, unexpected, if not perverse, in attitude, and almost equally acclaimed and objected to in the wide midland region to which he had taught, as the phrase was, the size of his foot—their friend had launched his bolt quite out of the blue and had thereby so shaken them as to make them fear almost more than hope. (James, "The Birthplace")

Mr. Grant-Jackson is a preponderant pushing person because he's been made by *p*'s, and the rhythm and phrasing of James's writing here prepares and perfectly presents him to us. Certainly we cannot think of Molly Bloom apart from her music, or the gay and rapid Anna Livia apart from hers.

If one examines the texture of a fiction carefully, one will soon see that some words appear to gravitate toward their subject, while others seem to emerge from it. In many works this logical movement is easily discernible and very strong. When a character speaks, the words seem to issue from him and to be acts of his. Description first forms a *nature*, then allows that nature to *perform*. We must be careful, however, not to judge by externals. Barkis says that Barkis is willing, but the expression *functions* descriptively to qualify Barkis, and it is Dickens' habit to treat speech as if it were an attribute of character, like tallness or honesty, and not an act. On the other hand, qualities, in the right context, can be transformed into verbs. Later in the book don't we perceive the whiteness of the whale as a design, an intention of Moby Dick's, like a twist of his flukes or the smashing of a small boat?

Whether Mr. Cashmore was once real and sat by James at someone's dinner table, or was instead the fabrication of James's imagination, as long as he came into being from the world's direction he once existed outside language. The task of getting him in, I shall call the problem of rendering. But it must be stressed (it cannot be stressed too severely) that Mr. Cashmore may never have had a model, and may never have been imagined either, but may have come to be in order to serve some high conception (a Mr. Moneybags) and represent a type, not just himself, in which case he is not a reality *rendered*, but a universal *embodied*. Again, Mr. Cashmore might have had still other parents. Meanings in the stream of words before his appearance might have suggested him, or he may have been the spawn of music, taking his substance from rhythm and alliteration.

So FAR I have been talking about the function of a character in the direct stream of language, but there are these two other dimensions, the rendered and the embodied, and I should like to discuss each briefly.

If we observe one of J. F. Powers' worldly priests sharpening his eye for the pin by putting through his clerical collar, the humor, with all its sharpness, lives in the situation, and quite incidentally in the words. One can indeed imagine Powers thinking it up independently of any ver-

bal formula. Once Powers has decided that it would be
funny to show a priest playing honeymoon bridge with
his housekeeper, then his problem becomes the technical
one of how best to accomplish it. What the writer must
do, of course, is not only render the scene, but render the
scene inseparable from its language, so that if the idea
(the chaste priest caught in the clichés of marriage) is
taken from the situation, like a heart from its body, both
die. Far easier to render a real cornfield in front of you,
because once that rendering has reached its page, the
cornfield will no longer exist for literary purposes, no one
will be able to see it by peering through your language,
and consequently there will be nothing to abstract from
your description. But with a "thought up" scene or situation, this is not the case. It comes under the curse of story.
The notion, however amusing, is not literary, for it might
be painted, filmed, or played. If we inquire further and
ask why Powers wanted such a scene in the first place, we
should find, I think, that he wanted it in order to embody
a controlling "idea"—at one level of abstraction, the world-
liness of the church, for instance. If he had nuns around
a kitchen table counting the Sunday take and listening to
the Cubs, *that* would do it. Father Burner beautifully
embodies just such a controlling idea in Powers' celebrated story "The Prince of Darkness." Both rendering
and embodying involve great risks because they require
working into a specific order of words what was not originally there. Any painter knows that a contour may only
more or less enclose his model, while a free line simply
and completely is. Many of the model's contours may be
aesthetically irrelevant, so it would be unwise to follow
them. The free line is subject to no such temptations. Its
relevance can be total. As Valéry wrote: There are no
details in execution.

Often novelists mimic our ordinary use of language. We
report upon ourselves; we gossip. Normally we are not
lying, and our language, built to refer, actually does.
When these selfsame words appear in fiction, and when
they follow the forms of daily use, they create, quite readily, that dangerous feeling that a real Tietjens, a real
Nickleby, lives just beyond the page; that through that

thin partition we can hear a world at love. But the writer must not let the reader out; the sculptor must not let the eye fall from the end of his statue's finger; the musician must not let the listener dream. Of course, he will; but let the blame be on himself. High tricks are possible: to run the eye rapidly along that outstretched arm to the fingertip, only to draw it up before it falls away in space; to carry the reader to the very edge of every word so that it seems he must be compelled to react as though to truth as told in life, and then to return him, like a philosopher liberated from the cave, to the clear and brilliant world of concept, to the realm of order, proportion, and dazzling construction . . . to fiction, where characters, unlike ourselves, freed from existence, can shine like essence, and purely Be.

A Pre-Raphaelite Ending:
Mrs. William Morris to Her Daughter

Richard Howard

For Sanford Friedman

London, 1915

Save it all; you do not know
the value things will come to have until
the world grows dim around you, and your things
—however doubtful in the changing light,
    things are what you have
    left. And all you have.
 Once the Zeppelins are gone
—and I shall be gone too, then, surely gone
out of this chair, this bed, this *furniture*,
there will be time enough to throw away
    whatever is left.
    Keep the papers here

in these boxes where I have
kept them so long to myself—for myself,
till the Zeppelins. I am not certain
(how could I be, kept here out of harm's way)
>   what Zeppelins are.
>   You would not expect
the daughter of an Oxford
livery-stable keeper to know it . . .
Your father was not fond of animals.
He said once he might get to like a horse,
>   if he had the time.
>   Take care with the ones
on top, they are photographs.
Read out what is scrawled there: "Dearest Janey,
Dodgson will be here tomorrow at noon,
do come as early as you can manage."
>   They have no backing
>   and break like dead leaves.
Often Gabriel painted
from these when he could not see me. He said
Mr. Dodgson knew what to leave out. Give
that one to me. No, it does not matter:
>   I want to hear you
>   say the words aloud:
"Absence can never make me
so far from you again as your presence did
for years. Yet no one seems alive now—
the places empty of you are empty
>   of all life." Of course
>   William knew of it,
but trusted. He had a deep
understanding of one side of life, and
invented the other. Remember how
he loved to list the things he owned,
>   grade and tabulate . . .
>   Why, he could not sit
in this room without an arm
about my waist—when others were by. Then
one time he burst out in a rage: "Is it
nothing but make-believe, am I no more
>   than Louis XVI
>   tinkering with locks?"
You know what his rages were—
I saw him drive his head against that wall,

making a dent in the plaster. "With locks,"
he said, "tinkering with locks, and too late . . ."
              With locks, did he say,
              or clocks? Clocks, I think.
How can a woman resolve
her marriage, save by lies? I have not learned
from others. I speak of my own life. She
stays at home, the man goes forth. A husband's
              absence, a daughter's
              anger, a lover's
suspicions—that is her lot.
What survives is the resistance we bring
to life, the courage of our features, not
the strain life brings to us. Each doctor says
              a different thing
              when I awaken
gasping in the night. How well
one has to be, to be ill! *Tragic health*,
Mr. Ruskin called it. That is his hand,
I recognize the stroke. He gave me this
              during a long walk
              after Gabriel
was cold in his grave, at last.
No one may see them till after my death,
and you must wait for that. William waited,
but I have not died. He came to Kelmscott
              —the meadows flooded
              that year, and the noise
of water filled the air. "Jane,
I wegwet," he said—he could not pronounce
his r's, odd in a man named Ruskin. Then
a tortoise-shell butterfly settled on
              my shoulder, but he
              refused to notice.
"I cannot admire any
lower in the scale than a fish," he said,
"I have the best disposition toward slugs
and gnats, but why they exist I do not
              understand." He stopped,
              though, to pick some cress
growing by the path—and what
he regretted was that he could not bear
to destroy these drawings he would give me
on the condition that I never look

at them in my life.
        They must be naked
drawings of me, beautiful
indeed if Mr. Ruskin could not burn
what he bought to keep the world and William
from seeing. There are his words on the seal:
           "I should as soon try
           finding fault with him
as with a nightshade-blossom
or a thundercloud. Of him and of these
all I can say is that God made him, and
they are greatly made. To me they may be
           dreadful or deadly.
           There is certainly
something wrong with him—awful
in proportion to the power it affects
and renders at present useless. So it was
with Turner, so with Byron." With this came
           a great quantity
           of ivory-dust
to be made into a jelly,
which it seems is an excellent physic
for invalids. Not even William failed
to guess the shame beneath the show—
           he had the habit,
           months and years after,
of taking up the packet
and regarding its black seal with the eye
of an enemy. I was like Mariana
in the moated grange, listening too often
           to the mouse shrieking
           in the wainscot. "I
can't paint you but I love you,"
he said that when I sat to them, at Oxford.
He first saw me there, and his destiny
was defined . . . Gabriel called him a name:
           Tops, the poetic
           upholstery-man.
Their mothers all outlived them—
Gabriel, William, *and* Mr. Ruskin.
It was an abyss then, an imbroglio
then and after. The reciprocal
           life of "well persons"
           grew impossible.

Moments come when the pattern
is laid before us, plain. And then we know
the limitations, accidentally
repeated, are the stuff of life. They will
                    return again, for
                    they are just . . . ourselves.
  Then we know that this and none
other will be our life. And so begins
a long decay—we die from day to dream,
and common speech we answer with a scream.
                  Put those things aside.
                  Here are the letters
  from Iceland, times were mended
for us both, by then. William was away
from the loud group of yellowing rowdies
who called themselves "communists"—and from me.
                  And he wrote, always,
                  lovely letters—if
you did not have to hear him
say the words, as if he were breaking off
bones, throwing them aside—it was, through him,
an ancient voice speaking, or a voice from
                  a previous life
                  jerking the words out
  of a body which it had
nothing to do with. Take one from the lot,
they are all the same, though like no one else:
freeing ourselves we forge our own chains.
                  "I lie often out
                  on the cliffs, lazy
  themselves, all grown with gold broom,
not athletic as at Dover, not gaunt
as at Shields, and through the mist of summer,
sea and sky are one, while just underfoot
                  the boats, together,
                  stand immovable—
  as if their shadows clogged them.
So one may lie and symbolize until
one falls asleep, and that be a symbol
as well." Take the last one. I remember
                  the last words the best.
                  "As for living, dear,
  people like those you speak of
don't know what life means or death either, save

for one or two moments when something breaks
the crust, and they act for the time as if
                              they were sensitive."
                              William's mind was set
  on things more significant
than human lives, individual lives . . .
During the last illness, Dolmetsch came here
to play Byrd to him on the virginals.
                              He broke into tears
                              —of joy, only joy
  at the opening phrases
of a pavane. Then he saw white bodies
moving, crowned and bound with gold. That faded.
I went for the post, and when I returned
                              he stifled the blood
                              streaming from his mouth
  and held fast to my gown, one
of his designs I had worn all those days.
"The clothes are well enough," were his last words,
"but where has the body gone?" Is there more
                              besides, in the box?
                              I thought not. Will you
  do as I say, save it all—
the rest of the things are mere images,
not medieval—only middle-aged:
lifelike but lifeless, wonderful but dead.
                              These are mine. Save them.
                              I have nothing save them.

The Adventure of the Mantises

Robert Chatain

I SHAVED, normally, at five o'clock, after dinner and before mail call, too early to observe the spectacle of insect and arachnid swarming in the eaves of the shower house around the naked light bulbs. Little had changed since January. The damp weather of the monsoon perhaps stimulated their activities, perhaps retarded them; I rarely noticed, by September, what was going on above my head as I scraped at my face with razor and cold water. Only when a web tangled in my hair did I sweep it away, breaking its mooring cables and sending its maker into glittering arthropod panic—"Hubris," I muttered, watching the spider flee through the ruins of its lair toward the safety of the green rafters. "Just keep the damned things within reason, that's all I ask." To destroy one of the webs always disturbed me, for I realized that, by catching their quota of flies and mosquitoes, the spiders in the eaves made it possible for us to stand still in front of the mirrors long enough to shave without cutting our throats.

Although the pageant in the rafters hadn't changed with the coming of the monsoon, there were noticeable additions to the rest of the insect world: now large, pallid moths with feathery wings could be found clinging to the dusty screens in early morning; black, ugly crickets were breeding by the thousands and appeared in all sizes, smaller than grasshoppers and as big as mice; mosquitoes thriving in the dampness infested the bunkers out on the perimeter; all the dogs carried ticks like brown buttons in their hair; ants, roaches, centipedes, and even scorpions moved from the teeming underbrush into the barracks, and many of us sprayed our blankets and shoes with insect repellent before going to bed. But the most interesting new arrival of the summer rainy season was the praying mantis, which, though rare at other times of the year, was present in patient, twiglike abundance during the monsoon. No doubt the extra thousands of other insects kept it fed, and possibly its young were hatched in those first gentle showers of late April and May.

The mantises usually preferred tall grasses or rank, green vegetation as their habitat, so I was surprised (startled, even) to see a small one, only two inches long, hanging from the wooden frame of the scratched mirror.

Its abdomen was thin, mottled brown in color, and the two pairs of legs supporting it were nearly microscopic, no thicker than strands of my own brown hair. The thorax bent up from the abdomen at a slight angle. The creature's head was a tiny triangle of light green, with the black spots of its eyes on the two top corners and its jaws, too small to be seen, at the bottom. From the center of the top side of the triangle, straight filaments of antenna sprouted upwards, following the angle of the head so that their tips were separated by an inch. The folded, serrated forelegs were attached to the top of the thorax. The insect carried them pressed together, raised in benediction, ready.

I examined it while the shaving cream evaporated on my skin. The body of the mantis swayed slightly on its long, fragile legs as the wind pushed at it. When I leaned closer to get a better view, the mantis raised its head to look back at me. Of all insects only mantises turn their heads directly toward their prey, as if they had bi-polar vision. I drew back. The mantis lowered its head and resumed its wait for food. I returned to shaving. When I bent to splash water from my tin bowl on my face I wondered briefly if there was a chance the mantis would leap down on me, into my hair. I would not be afraid. Mantises move slowly and with extreme dignity, as opposed to spiders, whose ghastly speed appalls me. But the mantis could hardly jump on those thin, delicate legs of its abdomen, and the two strong forelegs were too specialized for killing to serve its locomotion.

I washed myself clean and then I dried myself with a dark green towel, and after that I raised the towel and gently brought it near to the motionless insect. Holding a fold of it before the mantis' body, I moved the towel toward the insect, rolling the cloth out away from the mirror frame slowly until I had transferred the mantis (who had struck out once, tentatively, at the towel, then not fought the movement) from its perch to the folds of the towel. I was careful not to pull its legs free of the wood too quickly. When I had it in my hands I carried it to the waist-high wall of weathered sandbags surrounding the barracks and repeated the process in reverse, setting the insect down as gingerly as I had picked it up.

"What are you up to?" Crawford, from Ammunition Supply, appeared next to me. His own towel was around his neck and he held a bar of soap in his hand.

"A praying mantis," I explained.

"I can see that," said Crawford.

The mantis was slowly turning a lighter brown to match the bleached canvas fabric of the sandbags. Swaying, moving its legs one at a time in the only way it could make progress forward, it took two interminable steps. Crawford said, "They fly, don't they?"

"No. They used to fly. Those are vestigial wings, like beetles sometimes have, folded over the top of its abdomen. It can't fly any more."

"What happened to it?"

"No, you don't understand."

The mantis waited, as mantises spend their lives, waiting.

"I'm taking a shower," Crawford said, turning away. At that moment a black fly landed barely five inches from the mantis. I stiffened.

"Crawford! You've got to watch this. It's going to get a fly." Crawford came quickly. The mantis was leaning far forward on its legs, swaying violently as if a strong wind had arisen; with each swing of its body one of its legs moved slightly, until the mantis was within striking distance. With one last lean forward, it struck. The coiled forelegs moved too fast to be seen, but the fly escaped somehow, unharmed. Crawford and I groaned.

"Missed him, damn it."

"Did you see how quick he was?"

"Fantastic."

In the next few minutes no more flies landed on the sandbags, so Crawford went off to take his shower. I stood up, but instead of gathering my tin pan and razor and shaving cream to return to the barracks, I began wandering around the vicinity of my mantis, waving the towel to stir any flies in the area on the slight chance that one might land close to the patient hunter. I searched for roaches on the walls of the shower house but did not see any; I examined the grass of the drainage ditch for beetles; I upended boards and rocks, checking for crickets. Nothing. On its sandbag, the mantis still hadn't moved, so I continued to search. There were plenty of spiders, of course, most of them patching and repairing their webs in preparation for the night, when the bulbs over the washstand would be turned on and attract nocturnal flying insects, particularly the succulent, helpless moths. Did mantises eat spiders? The mantis I had was obviously a young mantis, not fully-grown, and these were rather large spiders, bloated from feasting; could my mantis handle one of them? I kept on looking for something else to feed it.

Turner saw me poking in the weeds under the boardwalk and asked what I was looking for.

"I dropped my Distinguished Service Cross down here somewhere," I answered.

"Your discharge, did you say?"

"Yes, that's what I meant."

Miller, a friend, came out of the barracks.

"Peter," I hailed him, "take a look at this." I led him to the mantis. "Praying mantis. He just missed a fly that landed near him a couple of minutes ago. I'm trying to stir up some action with a roach or a beetle, but I can't find anything. It's preposterous not to be able to find a cruddy insect when you need one."

"What is it?"

"A praying mantis. A baby," I added. "They come much bigger, even in the States. I've seen the things everywhere since the rains began."

"What about one of these spiders?" asked Miller.

"I don't know. All right, we can try it."

"Their webs are too high."

I picked up a stick. "I'll try to get one with this." I broke through a web and made a large circle around the spider in its center, trying to cut all the strands which it could use for escape so it would be forced to remain with the remnants of its web wound on the end of the stick. I was not quick enough; a few threads remained and the spider rushed to safety.

"Let me try it." Miller took the stick and cut into another web.

"You've got to get around him fast," I said.

He swooped the stick rapidly around the edge of the web, catching the spider in a tangle of its own silk.

"You've got him!"

The spider dangled from the stick.

"Now let's see if the mantis will go for him."

We moved toward the sandbags as the spider climbed up to the stick and paused, uncertain whether to move to the end of the wood or toward Miller's hand. Another man, come down to shower as Crawford had done, stopped to watch us. The spider had begun crawling toward Miller's hand when we reached the sandbags. He held the stick over our mantis and shook it, but spiders rarely fall.

"Hold it down here," I directed, "and let the spider crawl up to the mantis. They always head up rather than down." Miller stooped and tipped the stick up from his hand, touching the tip of it to the side of the sandbag, and the spider predictably climbed. The mantis remained perfectly still. The spider hesitated before it stepped off onto the sandbag where the mantis waited.

"Watch this," I whispered.

Suddenly the spider rushed from the stick past the mantis too quickly for it to react. My mantis cocked its head and moved one of its legs as if to begin ponderous chase, but the spider vanished over the far side of the sandbag wall.

"Damn!"

"That stupid son of a bitch, we've got to get another spider."

"Wait." We turned, and there behind us was Sergeant Stafford, engrossed. "Here comes the spider for another look."

The spider had come into sight again; not far from the mantis, although out of immediate range of its forelegs, the spider began a succession of strangely exaggerated motions, dipping and raising on its legs, turning in quick circles, then standing motionless, body arched high in the air. A near-invisible ribbon of silk bloomed from the tip of its abdomen and fluttered in the wind.

"Ah! He's letting a balloon fly! He'll feed out silk until it catches on something, then climb the strand and begin a new web. Look closely, you can see the thread."

Miller reached out with the stick. "I've got it." He caught the free end of the thread and held the stick steady. The spider tugged on the thread to test its hold and then climbed. Miller swung the stick quickly around and lowered the still-climbing spider toward the mantis. The silk brushed the bag and the spider fell free. The mantis leaned forward. The spider rushed away from the stick but toward the mantis. The mantis struck. The spider struggled out of the grip of the mantis' forelegs and fled away again over the edge of the sandbags.

"God damn!"

"This is one useless mantis."

"Wait a minute, he's got something." It was the leg and a piece of the spider's body that the mantis held to its jaws with his folded forelegs.

"Wow!"

"Let's get another spider."

"A mantis," I narrated, "is the only insect which will eat spiders." This was not true, of course, but I felt that a certain license was permissible. Peter and two of the others who had watched our mantis perform began waving sticks through spiders' webs everywhere they found them. Spiders dropped to the ground or ran frantically for the cracks in the side of the shower house. There was much shouting and laughter. "Mantises," I went on, "used to be able to fly, but that was millions of years ago; they traded wings for the specialization of their forelegs and the camouflage of their shape. They look just like twigs. Their whole life is standing still, blending with their surroundings, waiting for their prey. They're called praying mantises because of the attitude of their front legs while they wait. Actually they're among the most deadly of all the insects, to other insects, I mean; to man and animals they're harmless. Although I have read of a South American species which eats hummingbirds and mice. Mantises are also the strongest of the insects. Those front legs have quite a grip. Nothing else can catch spiders. Look at how young this one is, and that was a full-grown spider it dismembered."

"We've got a fly without killing it," crowed Gomez, approaching with his thumb and forefinger held out in front of him, pinched together on a black speck with writhing legs.

"Drop it right in front of the mantis," I said.

"No, wait a minute, it's still eating. Let it finish the pieces of the spider."

"No, it's all finished."

"Where should I drop it?"

"Hold it," shouted Warren, one of the clerks on the Judge Advocate General's staff, "the instant you let go of it the fly will take off. Pull off its wings before you drop it."

"Go to hell."

"What's the difference, you're going to feed it to the mantis anyway, pull its wings off."

"You do it."

"I'll do it," Miller said, "give it to me." The transfer of the struggling fly was managed with difficulty, but then Miller had it. Holding it a few inches from his eyes he ripped the wings from its body expertly.

"Now drop it."

He did.

The mantis was obviously interested, but delayed its strike, sensing something unnatural in its victim's sudden appearance. The fly lay still at first but then began flailing its thin black legs. The mantis lashed out mechanically.

"That's probably more food than a mantis normally eats in ten days," I commented.

"I'm going to look for another spider," said Williamson. There was quite a crowd around us now, most of them clad only in undershorts with towels thrown around their necks. Even the few people in the showers were standing up close to the screens, watching. On the stairs to the second floor of the barracks stood several more people. Miller and I were leaning forward, gazing at the mantis eating its meal. We kept our arms folded against our chests and swayed back and forth on our haunches as naturally as we could, to avoid annoying the mantis, gorging itself.

From behind the shower house Williamson gave a shout. "God, will you look at this! We've been wasting our time!"

We rushed over to see what he had found. There, on the ground, crouching on a piece of wire screen, was the biggest mantis I had ever encountered; bright green, impassive, eight inches in length, it stood on legs as thick as coat hangers. The head was so large that its mandibles could be seen, shining with saliva. We crowded closer.

"Pick it up."

"Carry it over to the sandbags."

"Let's put them both together, see what happens."

"No!" I had a certain emotional stake in the young mantis I had found on the wooden frame of my mirror. I knew that mantises were cannibals; mine wouldn't stand a chance. But Williamson grasped the section of screen and started toward the barracks.

My mantis was still eating. Williamson set the screen down upon the sandbags nearby, and stepped back.

We waited for the insects to notice each other. Overhead, two Thunderchiefs banked in close formation, beginning their descent to the runway at Bien Hoa. The sun had set and the air was full of shadows. Behind us the noise of the showers returned to normal, waterfalls of water, bare feet on wet boards, hands slapping soap across bodies.

Nothing was happening.

"Here." Miller reached out with his thumb and forefinger, the same thumb and forefinger he had used to tear the fly apart.

"Don't!"

"No, I'm just going to move it over by the little one," he said. The large mantis saw his hand come near and reared its thorax upwards, legs partially uncoiling. Miller hastily withdrew his hand.

"Will it bite?"

"It's going to take your finger off at the second knuckle."

"Probably not. It might pinch you with its arms but I don't think it will hurt."

"Be careful."

"Yes, be careful of the mantis, their legs break very easily."

"Reach around behind it," someone suggested.

Miller moved his hand slowly around behind the mantis' head. It followed his movement with its eyes until its head could turn no farther, then seemed to lose interest. Miller reached in and deftly took hold of the long, thin thorax just behind the head. He pulled it loose from the screen too quickly, I thought, but the insect seemed unharmed; it waved all of its legs in slow circles and opened the pale useless wings on its back as Miller lifted it through the air. He put it down practically on top of my small mantis, which instantly froze. The great mantis began walking, stumbling ponderously over the well-camouflaged smaller insect and traveling several feet down the sandbag wall before coming to rest again. One leg, I noticed, dragged limply behind it.

"You did break one of its legs," I accused, but Miller said "No, it was like that before."

Inability to Depict an Eagle

Richard Eberhart

The eagles have practically left America.
Pouncing on an unexpected small creature,
Their talons fierce, they pick him to pieces.
Those great soaring wings that make us rejoice
Eventuate the male eagle to the top of a tall pine
From which he surveys illimitable ocean waters,
Flounces down on a lower abrasive nest; sated,
He reposes. He does not know that he has been poisoned.
Man the subtle, man the unknown, man the two-legged,
Has poisoned the food that feeds the bald eagles.

A psychic subtlety addresses the situation.
I have lost control of the bird as he has lost control
Of his subsistence. With an amazement bordering on devo-
    tion
I held before the movie lens the seven-foot wingspan
As the eagle took off and soared out over the ocean,
Made his powerful return to alight on the tallest pine,
Then drop to the rough nest. Alone. Was his mate killed
By the bullet of some ruthless American for sport?
Were his soarings looking for food, or for mate?
Is my self-consciousness more significant than his ignorance?

I held his heart in my telescopic lens with love,
I watched him in admiration in the tall summertime.
He was without equal. He was great in the skies in my eyes,
Only likened in majesty to some suffering poet
Who surveys the brutal headlands but is crushed to death
Almost before the realization of his scope,
Or like some voyager in the secrets of the soul
Who astounds us with the vitality of his presence
But who, like Socrates, is unknown in the marketplace,
Or like Christ, never tells us how it was on the Cross.

Robert

Philip Levine

OCTOBER. From Simpson's hill
the great moon of stone
frowns in the rain. In the
fields below dark bruises
of spike stiffen into seed.
The cows are shuffling
behind me, back down
to the long chromium sheds
and the painless taking.

I watch an hour pass.
The darkness rises from
the floor of the valley
thickening the air between
branches, between stone
and tree, between my eyes
and what was here.

Now I'm in the dark.
I remember pages torn
from an automotive catalogue,
an ad once fallen from
heaven and hanging in
the city air—"It's never too late . . ."
If I follow my hands
will I feel the winter shake
the almonds into blossom?

Adam's Task

John Hollander

"*And Adam gave names to all cattle, and
to the fowl of the air, and to every
beast of the field . . .*"—Gen. 2:20

THOU, paw-paw-paw; thou, glurd; thou, spotted
 Glurd; thou, whitestap, lurching through
The high-grown brush; thou, pliant-footed,
 Implex; thou, awagabu.

Every burrower, each flier
 Came for the name he had to give:
Gay, first work, ever to be prior,
 Not yet sunk to primitive.

Thou, verdle; thou, McFleery's pomma;
 Thou; thou; thou—three types of grawl;
Thou, flisket; thou, kabasch; thou, comma-
 Eared mashawk; thou, all; thou, all.

Were, in a fire of becoming,
 Laboring to be burned away,
Then work, half-measuring, half-humming,
 Would be as serious as play.

Thou, pambler; thou, rivarn; thou, greater
 Wherret, and thou, lesser one;
Thou, sproal; thou, zant; thou, lily-eater.
 Naming's over. Day is done.

How Does That Garden Grow

Frederick Busch

TAP CAME DOWNSTAIRS in the early morning, before gold light lay on the windows like a brilliant steady sound, and Carrie was in the livingroom chair, the bridge lamp on behind her, and a steam of cigarettes up in the parchment funnel that cherished brightness away from the still house.

"Carrie," he said.

She looked at him and said, "I didn't hear you up, Daddy. How do you feel?"

"Are you smoking or reading?"

"Daddy, I forgot the coffee. Getting *stupid* now."

"Can't you tell me which?"

"I'm sorry, I forgot the coffee, let me put it up. And eggs, I can boil some."

"Do you know?"

"And make some toast."

"Alright."

"Daddy."

"No, goddammit, that is fine. You have a right to sit there, this is our house."

"Please. Daddy, please."

"No. Damn, I can't shut up. I never can keep my mouth closed. I'll be down for coffee in a little bit. You take your time, I'll be washing out my floppy mouth."

He went back up the short flight of stairs that didn't bend, that disappeared into shallow disappearing darkness; his back was long, and his robe was bright and long on his legs, and his climbing was a marvel of the appetite of dark: that tall bright man and his gleaming head, seized and squeezed away by a little chill of black.

Carrie reached back over the top of the chair and turned

the lamp off. "Terrible," she said, and turned the lamp back on. She said, "It's worse," and then she said, "So what," and stood—in front of the chair, across from the yellow-covered sofa looking dirty in the dark, away from the bookshelves crooked as wasting teeth along the wall where the front door was, and in a room where paper on the floor could make the furniture seem to slide from place—and said, again, "So what. It's morning, hurray for birds."

She walked through a wide door to the kitchen and stood in the doorway, small in the doorway and smaller in the grains of darkness, flatfoot, pale, and then she moved, without the lights on, at pots and water, cups—things that sang on the morning's solid stillness and made the ring of the hour change.

Light grew on the back-wall windows and, like bubbles of water, swelled fat until it burst inside and the little kitchen lightened: silver on the shiny surfaces, then gold on old wood and dull linoleum, and gold yet for minutes with a hint or threat from fields and sky of wheat and wetness, and merely light then, and then just morning. Carrie sat at the white-ringed wooden table, pushing pottery cups into place, grinding a steel spoon in the sugar dish, moving the pitcher of milk in a small circle, and the percolator thumped on the slightly canted stove, the fat refrigerator hummed at the backyard door, and the ceiling squeaked again and again as Tap, upstairs, where light had come in too, was moving into the day.

Carrie stood and walked to the wall-hung phone and, without lifting the receiver, dialed, around and again, around and again, standing at the telephone and dialing no exchange, just making clicks. The floor upstairs squeaked to a pace, then, and Tap came down the stairs and through the door, all heavy hanging gabardine and starched white shirt, the striped tie, frayed where he had knotted and knotted in early mornings, choking up his lean throat.

"Baby," he said, "what do you want from the phone?" Carrie turned with a smile that showed her teeth. "You want to get through to me, you can pour that fine-smelling coffee for us. Sit down here and drink some coffee with me."

So they sat in the bright room on facing sides of the

wooden table, Tap with his back straight, lifting coffee with a smooth uncomplicated move, and Carrie was rounded low in the chair, her cup wobbling as coffee rolled to stain the rim. She looked at the table, and Tap—bald and polished, lean—was looking at her. The wood of the house made its sounds; refrigerator drummed its cycles; and they sat, they looked ahead or down, ahead and down, and drank their coffee and sat.

Then Carrie said, "I'll make some toast," and moved away, to the counter by the sink.

Tap said, "Good. Fine." He filled his cup and drank up steam.

Carrie stood at the counter and said, "Why did you get up early, Daddy? Couldn't you sleep last night? I looked at you, I thought you were asleep."

"Oh sure. Sure. Yes, it was good sleeping weather I thought. Didn't you? Wasn't it?"

"Nice and chilly to start with."

"Yes."

"It got kind of warm later on, though."

"Yes, I think it did."

"Just like spring, it felt."

"Well——"

"That's how it got to feeling later on."

"Real early in the day?"

"That's right."

"Yes, well you get that often, in the mornings near to March. But I can't think of a spring that started like this. This early."

"But it could."

"Yes."

"Couldn't it?"

"Yes, sweetheart, I think so. Yes it could."

"And that's why you came down."

"I guess."

"Isn't that why?"

"Carrie, I suppose."

"Did you come to drink, Daddy?"

"Oh now."

"I don't care."

"That makes it pretty dramatic. Doesn't it? I don't think

I'm a very dramatic man. Not that way. Not a guzzle at five in the morning, honey. Not your square old man. Don't cry."

"No. I'm not."

"I hope you won't. You can, I can't forbid a thing like that with my big old stupid mouth, honey. Of course you can. I really hope you won't right now."

"I'm not."

"I know."

"I'm not."

"I have a meeting in the afternoon, a curriculum meeting. The social studies consultant is coming in from Syracuse to tell us how to handle communism this year. The party line on the party. You know? I tell them 'Teach it from the newspapers,' but that's too much like being alive for them. A little frightening. So they keep looking for a book that says the right things they want the kids to know in the tenth grade. You know those birds."

"Sure."

"A bunch of farmers. They have no business inside anybody's classroom. Farmers is what they are. I wonder if they *read* the papers."

"Daddy."

"What, girl of me mornings, would you have of me today?"

"Do you think it's spring? Please. Tell me what you think. I want to know if you think it's spring."

"So I'll call you later on how late I'll be. Okay?"

"*No! No!* Please, Daddy. It's early spring, admit it. Say it is! It's early spring this year, that's why you came down this morning. Isn't it? Please."

"Carrie, why don't you carry that plateful of toast over here, and bring a jar of jelly, and sit down and have some breakfast with me? Come on. Come over here. I won't call up." He broke a slice of toast in ragged halves and spread a piece with bright blue jelly, wiping the knife hard and neat on the edge of the bread, placing the toast gently on Carrie's saucer and licking clean the clean dull blade of the knife. "I won't call up," he said. "Isn't that it? The calling?"

She nodded and looked at her lap.

"Alright," he said. "I won't call up, so you don't have to think it's the home. But I think it's spring, you're right. And I think we'll get the call. They do it quickly. As early as they can. They work that fast."

"I know."

"And I told you all I could when they died, sweetheart. Do you know that? I told you everything I could. I offered then to pay them extra if they'd do the burying right away. Did you know that? Because I said it all then and I knew it. I knew I wouldn't have a decent word to let you have. But winter is winter. Frozen ground is frozen ground. I couldn't make it warm up then and I can't freeze it now. I wanted to do something about that, but I couldn't. I regret that, Carrie. You're my girl, you know that. But I can't control the way the seasons work. And nobody reasons a gravedigger. If he tells you that the ground stays closed, the ground stays closed. When he tells you it's open, the ground is opened up. That's all."

"Do they keep them on ice?"

"I think so."

"Like meat."

"Baby——"

"Right, Daddy?"

"Yes. Like meat."

"All frozen. Blue, maybe."

"I guess."

"And they wait for the ground to thaw and they call you up——"

"It doesn't mean they'll call today, honey. Maybe it isn't even spring. What can you know about winter being done?"

"And they call you up and they say, 'Hi there, folks. Why, it's spring and we wondered if you can get up here and plant those old blue stiffed-up corpses today? Will you tell your father, Miss, when he gets home? The wife and infant are ready to plant. We're thawing them now.'" Her face was in her hands and her body moved. In the bright clear light, against the stiffened shadow of her father, Carrie's body moved.

"Baby," he said.

She said, "Daddy, why *did* you? Why did you have to have another kid?"

He put his hands on the edge of the table and held. "We didn't plan for that to happen, Carrie. You know that."

"Well how can you screw without *using* something? Daddy, *I* know that. You mean I've taken better care than you?" Her body stilled, his hands came off the table. "Well," she said. "Well." Then she said, "Oh Daddy."

He said, "Yes."

"Daddy, please."

"Yes. Well, Carrie, I suppose you've taken better care than Mother did. I seized her on an afternoon and no one thought. Do you understand that? That we didn't think? That we weren't thinking? It was what happened to us."

"Daddy, I'm sorry."

"Also the blood between her legs was what happened to us. The baby and the blood and driving forty miles to the hospital. It wasn't like the blood on sheets, it was shiny red. Very bright blood. She got whiter and her lips were black, it was *bright* blood and that's what happened. You understand? Carrie? Do you understand? I'm sorry. It's what happened to us. She shook. She felt very cold. I think I told you that."

"I'm sorry."

"I know."

"Daddy, I'm sorry."

"Baby, it's what happened. Alright now. Alright. Alright."

"I'm sorry."

"That's right." He stood, he walked, with his body straight, around to where she sat and said, "That's right. How could we be sorrier? It's spring, and the ground is getting soft. That's right. That's right." He stood behind her and cupped her neck and rubbed, rubbed.

"I'm not loose," she said.

He smiled and said, "I know."

"I'm not."

"I never thought you were. You know that. All you are is mine. You know?"

"I'm sorry."

"Yes."

"I am."

"That's right," he said. "That's right."

"I wish it wasn't spring," she said.

"I know."

She leaned back at his hands in the bright and ocher room and said, "I wish it could still be winter."

"Yes."

"With snow, and the ground frozen. With nothing to grow. Just white."

"I know," he said. "Just white." He rubbed his hand slowly in her hair and stepped away. "Do you want me to stay home today? Will you feel better if I stay at home?"

She looked ahead. "You said they wouldn't call," she said. "You don't think they'll call us up."

"No, baby. Not today. They won't call us today. We're clear."

"Then don't stay home. Go teach."

"I'll come home for lunch if you like. Or we can meet —I'll take you to lunch, how's that? We can meet in town and walk around together and find something to laugh at. All the french fries you want."

"At noon?"

"A little after."

"Five hours that is."

"I can try to leave early."

"Still. Five hours. Sure: yes, yes. I'll walk downtown and meet you at the school. In five hours."

"And the phone won't ring. It isn't really spring today, I think it really isn't. Not yet. Soon, but not yet, Carrie. We've got some time."

"Oh, Daddy, I don't think we have too much."

"We've got a little," he said. He walked back around to his chair, the body straight, and sat. He poured the dark brown coffee and looked at her face and smiled. "A last cup this morning with you, eh?" He reached across the table and poked a long finger, said, "Eat that piece of toast, Carrie, here we go," and picked up his half—dark brown, rigid, dry—and brought it to his mouth and nodded in the early liquid light and bit and chewed, and she did too.

No More Soft Talk

Diane Wakoski

DON'T ASK a geologist about rocks.
Ask me.

That man,
he said.

What can you do with him?
About him?
He's a rock.

No, not a rock,
I said.
        Well,
a very brittle rock, then.
One that crumbles easily, then.
Is crushed to dust, finally.

Me,
I said.
I am the rock.
The hard rock.
You can't break me.

I am trying to think how a woman
can be a rock,
when all she wants is to be soft,
to melt to the lines
her man draws for her.

But talking about rocks
intelligently
must be
talking about different kinds
of rock.

What happens to the brain
in shock? Is it

like an explosion
of flowers and blood,
staining the inside
of the skull?

I went to my house,
to see my man,
found the door locked,
and something I didn't plan
on—a closed bedroom door
(my bed)
another woman's handbag on the couch.
Is someone in the bedroom?

Yes, Yes,
a bed full of snakes all bearing new young,
a bed of slashed wrists,
a bed of carbines and rifles with no ammunition,
a bed of my teeth in another woman's fingers.

Then the answer to rocks,
as I sit here and talk.

The image of an explosion:
a volcanic mountain
on a deserted pacific island.
What comes up,
like gall in my throat,
a river of abandoned tonsils that can no longer cry,
a sea of gold wedding rings and smashed glasses,
the lava, the crushed and melted rock
comes pouring out now,
down this mountain you've never seen,
from this face that believed in you,
rocks that have turned soft,
but now are bubbling out of the lips of a mountain,
into the ocean raising the temperature
to 120 degrees.
If your ship were here
it would melt all the caulking.

This lava,
hot and soft,
will cool someday,
and turn back into the various stones.
None of it is

my rock.
My rock doesn't crumble.
My rock is the mountain.
Love me
if you can.
I will not make it easy for you
anymore.

Gretel in Darkness

Louise Glück

THIS IS THE WORLD we wanted. All who would have
      seen us dead
Are dead. I hear the witch's cry
Break in the moonlight through a sheet of sugar.
    God rewards.
Her tongue shrivels into gas. . . .

                              Now, far from women's
                                  arms
And memory of women, in our father's hut
We sleep, are never hungry.
Why do I not forget?
My father bars the door, bars harm
From this house, and it is years.

No one remembers. Even you, my brother,
Summer afternoons you look at me as though you meant
To leave, as though it never happened.
But I killed for you. I see armed firs,
The spires of that gleaming kiln—
    come back! come back!

Nothing changes. Nights I turn to you to hold me
But you are not there. Am I alone? Spies
Hiss in the stillness; Hansel, we are there still,
    and it is real, real,
That black forest and the fire in earnest.

Technicians and Troubadours:
How We Lost the Sex-Lab War

Benjamin DeMott

THE WORLD OF MIND divides itself, scientists and humanists berating each other in extravagances, competing destructively in situations that cry out for harmonious collaboration—where can a student find models of humane, wholistic concern?

The world of mind, building on foundations laid in the nineteenth century, develops detailed new knowledge with significance for the well-being of millions, and then allows reductionism, timidity, and vanity to deflect the passage of this knowledge to the public—how much can be said for contemporary intellectual life?

A story with bearings on these questions begins in 1954 with the decision of a young associate professor of obstetrics and gynecology at the Washington University Medical School to enter a new field: the laboratory study of human sexual response. The story ends with the announcement not many weeks ago by the same professor, Dr. William Masters, that his project's most hugely publicized piece of equipment—a plastic mechanical phallus—had been "disassembled," no plans in mind "for reconstruction." In the decade and a half between the decision and the disassembling, scores of sages, sexmongers, poets, and culture critics held forth in print on sex research, confusing issues or inventing them, distracting attention from significant realities of the subject. And, in the same period, the researchers themselves poured out a series of charges and simplistic rationales which obscured (and still obscure) the best uses and meanings of their undertaking.

The most tendentious of their charges was that the so-called literary or high-cultural view of human sex—every view, in short, that underemphasizes sex as physical activity pointed toward orgasmic release—is a lie that urgently requires scientific straightening out. The Washington University scientists didn't take this aggressive line publicly at the inception of their research; they took no line, for their chief concern at that time was to avoid a break in the voluntary press blackout about the sex lab, which, as it developed, the St. Louis newspapers and wire services maintained into the sixties. But once they felt safe, they hit hard. Dr. Masters' earliest paper on sex research, a 1960 report appearing in the *Western Journal of Surgery,* lashed out at "literary fiction and fantasy" in the area of sexual relations on the ground that it perpetuates an "unbelievable hodgepodge of conjecture and falsehood." In 1964 came the full-scale formal report of Masters' Reproductive Biology Research Foundation, published under the title *Human Sexual Response,* which was presented, jaw out, as a compendium of "physiologic truth as opposed to cultural fiction." And even at the present late hour, the sex researchers are still pressing an attack, in interviews and essays, against bookish "traditionalists" whose chat about love and "mystery" foists (they say) "an incredible amount of misconception, fantasy, and fallacy" upon people, nourishing "superstition and myth" and weakening the sense of fact.

PREDICTABLY, LITERARY TYPES took unkindly to this abuse, and counterattacked even before publication of *Human Sexual Response.* A characteristic salvo was Leslie Farber's "I'm Sorry, Dear," printed in *Commentary* in 1964. Since the author was himself a psychiatrist and a former chairman of the Association of Existential Psychology and Psychiatry, the assault looked at first glance more internecine than two-cultural. The manner and matter of the piece, however, together with the circumstances of its publication, established that Farber spoke as a humanist. "I'm Sorry, Dear" came decorated with a multitude of literary epigraphs and allusions (C. S. Lewis, Herman Melville, the Marquis de Sade, Lionel Trilling, and Eleanor of Aquitaine figured in one way or another). The essay opened, moreover, with a page of novelistic dialogue, the conversation of a couple just following an unsatisfactory episode of lovemaking, and was composed in a fashionable literary tone (both sternly Sartrian and sniffish).[1]

The minor charges in Farber's critique of Masters and Johnson were that their sexology (1) made "both the brothel and pornography less exciting dwellings for our erotic investigation," (2) removed the erotic life from "the traditional disciplines, such as religion, philosophy, literature, which had always concerned themselves with sex as human experience," (3) was preoccupied with gadgetry "at the expense of any imaginative grasp of the occasion" of love, and (4) was sick with democratic zeal (Masters believes, said Farber, that "the more minute physiological developments [in lovemaking] should belong to every citizen," and he increases "the political clamor for equal rights for women"). The major charges were, first, that the new sexology had in effect "invented" the orgasm as the essential part of woman's—and man's—whole sexual experience (in olden days "the moment of orgasm was not abstracted . . . and idealized," and was only an "occasional" part of the experience); and, second, that the sexologists denied Original Sin, encouraged lovers "to will the perfection on earth which cannot be willed," and thereby brought upon men "the pathos which follows all such strivings toward heaven on earth."

Important as the charges were, though, and frequent as their reiteration soon became, neither Farber's nor any subsequent literary response to the sexological crusade against "myth" was, in a decisive sense, a matter of specific charges. The literary mind built its case more through tone, nuance, implication, than through discrete, answerable arguments. The impression conveyed was that sex research was merely an aspect of the decline or collapse of Western culture. Farber and other *soi-disant* humanists adopted a voice of

[1] In explaining his belief that "sex for the most part has lost its viability as a human experience," Farber cited modern man's self-conscious, willful alienation from his own physicality, and rehearsed an argument about knowing and being known through sex that was taken directly, without acknowledgment, from Sartre's *Being and Nothingness*.

ironic resignation which spoke at every moment—regardless of the ostensible subject—of the "inevitability" in a dying culture of an endless succession of corruptions. They presented themselves as yearners for transcendence, people with a fastidious, half-*spirituelle* distaste for physicality and sensuality. And they constantly played off ideals and glories of past (imaginary) worlds of love against the base actualities of the modern sex-research lab.

Farber himself concentrated on the central figures of Arthurian romance (Queen Guinevere, Sir Galahad) and on the intense, delicate doctrines of courtly love in setting up the contrast. Others ranged farther. The English poet and novelist David Holbrook, for example, writing about "The Delusions of Sexology" in the *Cambridge Review*, invoked Duns Scotus, the medieval philosopher who scorned "imperfect love . . . 'love of concupiscence' . . . because it seeks the other for advantage." And the American novelist George P. Elliott, for another, harked back, in the *Hudson Review*, to heroic love affairs in Proust, reminding his reader of the refinement of Swann's feelings "as the phrase from Vinteuil's sonata is evoking tender memories of the days when Odette was in love with him."

ALL, HOWEVER, USED these models of elegance, decorum, discipline, and superhuman grace from the cultural past for a similar purpose, that of dramatizing the slobbishness of sex-research science. Think of Guinevere, think of Galahad, Farber told his audience, and then think of people tasteless enough to welcome the "prospect of arriving at the laboratory at 10:00 A.M., disrobing, stretching out on the table and going to work in a somewhat business-like manner while being measured and photographed. . . . (Thank you, Miss Brown, see you same time next week.)" Think, said the novelist Elliott, think of marvelous Swann and Odette, and then think of a "sane, taxpaying, tenured professor solemnly copulating with his wife on a cot in [the] laboratory, their arms strapped for blood-pressure readings, cathodes at their temples, cardio-tachographs zigging, their anuses wired, 'My bunny, my love, O sweetest

joy!' Well, every man has the right to make himself look
like a fool."

Imagine, said Holbrook, imagine the dignity and re-
straint of Scotus' mind engaged on its analysis of love, and
then:

> Imagine . . . a group of scientists making the Masters-
> Johnson color film of a female masturbating: the faceless
> torso, the arm, the moving fingers, the erotic flush on the
> thighs, the moistening organ, the stiffening nipples, the
> physical contractions of orgasm, the fine film of sweat
> covering the whole body afterwards. Or imagine for that
> matter the group of overalled scientists observing dials,
> with a camera team working on a man and woman who
> have coition (having never met before) on the labora-
> tory couch for a research fee. Sometimes the scientists
> stop them to make adjustments or measurements: then
> when they get going again the instruments are all set to
> time the physical features of orgasm: How often? How
> long? How many sperms? How acid or alkali? How strong
> is the ejaculation? Where did it go? Do the sperms sur-
> vive? Do the participants punch one another in their
> final ecstasy?

On both sides of the Atlantic dozens of other writers—
panelists, reviewers of the Masters-Johnson volume, letters-
to-the-editor men—echoed the literary complaint that a
monstrous new vulgarity was poisoning the land.

As should be said, Masters and Johnson were not the
only sexologists of the period who provided materials for
abuse. The earlier Kinsey, or pollster, school of research
was still active in the mid-sixties, and produced several
mockably "quantified" statements of its findings—witness
the following passage from a paper of a San Diego psy-
chologist:

> Both men and women engage in the more serious types
> of sex play as the type of dating involvement increases.
> The men, however, are significantly more liberal in their
> actual conduct particularly for the first few dates (NoK,
> N, PAWPBW, SI, $X^2 = 16.22$ 3df, p<1 percent), fre-
> quent and continuous dating (NoK, N, PAWPBW, SI,
> $X^2 = 14.62$ 3df, p<1 percent), and going steady (KN,
> PAW, PBW, SI, $X^2 = 15.62$, 3df, p<1 percent). . . .
> [R. L. Karen, "Some Variables Affecting Sexual Atti-

tudes, Behavior and Inconsistency." The paper included a key to symbols: N = nothing. K = kissing. PAW = petting above waist. PBW = petting below waist, etc.]

And as also should be said, there were occasions throughout the sixties when the ranks of literary antisexologists were swelled by writers who were cruder than the crudity they damned. The commonest offender was the popular novelist—a cluster of sex research novels appeared in the late sixties—and the reason for this was simple. Novels on the subject tsk-tsked and looked grave about the laboratory experiments, delivering short essays at key moments on lubricity, dehumanization and such. Yet commercial exigency dictated that events inside the labs be depicted with seemly fullness, and this requirement set up counterstrains.

Consider for instance Robert Kyle's *Venus Examined* (1968). The implied argument of the book is that the ordinary stuff of life (and of novelese)—personal relations—cannot be kept out of the sex lab, despite the avowals and high intentions of the researchers. (In Kyle's sex lab, the volunteers fall in and out of love with each other, arrange secret meetings, seek to seduce their scientist-observers, etc.) The overt argument—its spokesman is an English prof at Barnard who sits on the board of a foundation asked to fund the (electrical) phallus—echoes the standard charges:

> Your laboratory isn't the only place in the modern world where numbers have replaced names, where a machine is substituted for a living person, where action is separated from feeling and no act has any consequences. But somehow your modernity is a little more vivid! To me your copulation machine stands as a symbol of the other evil things that are being done to us in the name of science. It's too perfect! How skillfully it gives a woman her orgasmic relief, carrying her out of the frustrations and compromises of ordinary life into a condition of perpetual spasm. . . .

The conclusion of the book is a wild passage of new Luddite-ism that might have been—in the hands, say, of Nathanael West—a compelling bit of contemporary terror: a volunteer, bitter because discharged from the project, returns to the sex lab, smashes the copulation machine, and is herself electrocuted in the act.

But, to repeat, the various novelistic indictments of tastelessness, crudity, and vulgarity lacked force because of the density of vulgarity surrounding them in their own pages. In *Venus Examined* there are interminable discussions—not comically intended—about whether a lady who's *lost* her orgasmic capacity after participating in the project should sue the projectors. (" 'You never had trouble having orgasms before, and we can prove that from Prescott's own records. . . . You could . . . sue him,' Anne said. . . . 'Would you turn down half a million bucks? They give that much for a leg.' ") And a leering clumsiness marks nearly every episode of intercourse observed.

Pots calling kettles black weren't the only factor adding to the confusion. A dozen conflicting unconscious attitudes and prejudices figured in the arguefying between "humanist" and sex scientist from the start—elitism vs. egalitarianism, love of the past vs. optimism about the future, the sense of style and discipline vs. the relish of spontaneity and improvisation, nostalgia for religious passion vs. delight in the end of superstition. And stock responses were everywhere the rule. The literary man told his audience that the scientist operated under the delusion that the isolatable, observable, physiological act was the *only* act of love—a delusion betraying irremediable inward coarseness. The scientist told his audience that if his idea of sex was limited, at least he believed sex existed. Nobody on his side ever claimed, he said, as the poet Holbrook claimed, that "there is really no such thing as sex." ("There is only," Holbrook added, "the use of the sexual capacities of individuals to express potentialities of being.") Nor had anybody on his side ever denied, as Farber seemed to, that female frustration was real. (Until recently, Farber maintained, the unorgasmic woman had been "content with the mystery and variety of her difference from man, and in fact would not have had it otherwise.")

Trampled under by the rhetorical exchanges were a few genuine and discussable differences of assumption and value—but these were seldom in direct view. The antagonists spoke as though convinced that the proper aim for each was the complete discrediting, if not destruction, of the

other. Not only did they show small consciousness of the
root causes of the furies to which they were giving utter-
ance, they appeared not even to have considered asking
the most pertinent question: What in this instance will victory or defeat for either of us mean to everyone else?

On BOTH SIDES the root causes of the furies just mentioned are, of course, various. Jealousy is in the equation,
and snobbishness, and resentment about lost eminence and
power, and scorn for private metaphor allowed to go public and pass itself off for ages as truth. But there are other,
less frequently noted items as well. Not the least of these,
on the literary side, is the humanist's custom of abstracting
science from general cultural history—treating particular
scientific enterprises as unique phenomena, assuming that
while this or that "controversial" experiment may conceiv-
ably "belong" to some special field of science, such work
has no natural or logical place in the mainstream of liberal
humane inquiry. Again and again the assumption has
proved false, and the present episode is no exception. The
case is that sex-lab research is a direct result (others are
beyond counting) of a long struggle waged by scientific
and literary minds on behalf of the cause of intellectual
inclusiveness—a struggle begun in the nineteenth century
and still unfinished. Had the struggle not been waged,
neither the Masters and Johnson investigation, nor that of
Kinsey over a decade ago, could have been imagined,
much less conducted. And both probes will probably soon
impress more as markers of the progress of that cause than
for their particular findings.

To say this isn't to imply that Dr. Masters is a major
intellect or that the cause of inclusiveness flourished because those who created it worked together in conscious
coalition. Marx in the Manchester factories, Darwin gazing
at a gang of Fijians, Frazer teasing out the meaning of the
sacred grove at Nemi in *The Golden Bough*, Freud inter-
preting dreams and explaining displacement in the *Introductory Lectures on Psychoanalysis*, Lawrence creating
Mellors, Joyce creating Molly Bloom—these aren't thinkers in league. But a unity of effect can be felt in their

work: [2] they put men in touch with a range of material (behavior, values, symbolic acts, words, modes of feeling, thinking, and perceiving) lying outside the official culture of the day—materials establishing that human reality, present or historic, wasn't fully represented in official images. And the demand for fuller representation has grown ever more insistent throughout this century. Comparative study of cultures and value systems, inquiry into the parallel evolution of man and animal, the development of psychoanalysis, new models of social and economic history, genetical research in the fields of art and literature—these and numberless other undertakings are directly traceable to the whetted appetite for news of the prefatory, disorderly, just possibly basic states of being which established culture ignored.

From which it follows that treating the Masters and Johnson concept as a running down of intellectual energy, a symptom of contemporary irrationalism or decline of mind, is senseless. The project had honorable links with a dignified intellectual past, and, depending on the quality of its execution, it could have become an embodiment, minor but useful, of the best intellectual aspirations of the age. The current habit of culture is either to turn away from sexual intercourse, accounting it a private act, or to exploit it in public entertainment for commercial profit; both practices worsen social and moral problems, and contribute nothing to knowledge. Well enough, let us gaze straight at sexual intercourse, take it in as a definable, separable, natural phenomenon among phenomena—an act or event whose characteristics can be discerned, measured,

[2] A favored trick of the antisexologist was to deny this unity and dissociate literary men from the great changes of attitude and understanding brought about in the last century. Farber, for instance, claimed that literary artists who dealt with sex in their works thought of it in terms of "qualities such as modesty, privacy, reticence, abstinence, chastity, fidelity, shame." (Blake? Strindberg? Ibsen? Yeats?) Nowhere did he acknowledge that the accepted meanings of these terms have changed markedly in the last century and a half, or that literary men were themselves responsible in large measure for the redefinitions.

and compared. And let us maintain that same perspective over the entire field of sexual behavior—physiological response to pornography, masturbatory orgasms, homosexual experience, the experience of the prostitute. Let us seek plain truth here, on the ground that it has value in itself, and has occasionally proved of use in encounters with "social problems."

Granted, the Masters-Johnson project had comical as well as "shocking" aspects. The researchers shared the Yankee preoccupation with know-how; the passages in *Human Sexual Response* in which a personal voice (a hint of scoffing) cuts through the neutralism are usually those critical of false know-how:

> Most marriage manuals advocate the technique of finding the clitoris and remaining in direct manual contact with it during attempts to stimulate female sexual tensions. In direct manipulation of the clitoris there is a narrow margin between stimulation and irritation. If the unsuspecting male partner adheres strictly to marriage manual dictum, he is placed in a most disadvantageous position. He is attempting proficiency with a technique that most women reject during their own automanipulative experience.

Granted too, Masters and Johnson, like many other scientists, exemplified the national relish of technological gimmickry; the society of charcoal filters and poptops was reflected in the copulation machine:

> The artificial coital equipment was created by radiophysicists. The penises are plastic and were developed with the same optics as plate glass. Cold-light illumination allows observation and recording without distortion. The equipment can be adjusted for physical variations in size, weight, and vaginal development. The rate and depth of penile thrust is initiated and controlled completely by the responding individual. As tension elevates, rapidity and depth of thrust are increased voluntarily, paralleling subject demand. The equipment is powered electrically.

But the "Americanism" of the St. Louis project isn't in every respect comic. There are some notable national elements in the research that only the most priggish literary aristocrat could take as ludicrous; they're especially vivid in the passages of *Human Sexual Response* recounting the life history and sexual experience of some participants in the project—passages that chronicle a movement from emptiness to light.

CONSIDER THE CASE of Subject D, a "34-year-old male, married 6 years and the father of two children." An only child, a minister's son, father now dead, mother a receptionist for a doctor. Profession: draftsman. College: two years. Reason for dropout: death of the father. "There is a history of strict parental control during the teenage years, and an excessive concern for social mores." No "auto-manipulative history" (meaning masturbation) until freshman year in college, and this single experimental episode was followed for a full year by a "severe guilt residual." Sophomore year an episode of petting leads once to "involuntary ejaculation, with the experience followed for several months by residual guilt feelings." For four or five years afterward: prostitutes and masturbation, prostitutes and masturbation. Then Subject D marries. His bride is a business school graduate. There is a record of relative failure in coition, though neither partner is lacking in desire. Years pass. The couple hears of the Masters and Johnson research and makes inquiry:

> For orientation, five episodes were necessary after team interrogation. The first exposure was to background and equipment; during the second, coition was attempted without ejaculatory success. The third episode developed as successful coition for Subject D, but his wife was not orgasmic. During the fourth session both husband and wife were successful in individual automanipulative episodes, and in the fifth episode no difficulty was encountered by either partner in response to coital or manipulative stimuli. This pattern of freedom from restraint has been the rule in subsequent program exposure, much to the surprise of both husband and wife. The family has cooperated with long-range response-evaluation and male physiology programs . . .
> . . . Subject D was concerned with his own overcontrolled background, lack of sexual experience, and a

considered degree of sexual repression. When his wife first joined the program her orgasmic incidence was reported as rare with coital exposure but consistent with manipulation. Subsequent to working in the program her orgasmic achievement during coition has risen to the 80 percent frequency level. She has not been multi-orgasmic either during coition or automanipulation.

Subject D's wife has stated repeatedly that subsequent to program participation her husband has been infinitely more effective both in stimulating and in satisfying her sexual tensions. He in turn finds her sexually responsive without reservation. Her freedom and security of response are particularly pleasing to him. Together they maintain that they have gotten a great deal more out of cooperation with the program than they have contributed, and they wish to continue on a long-term basis.

THE LITERARY MIND, the figure of style and breeding, may smile at such a recital, shaking his head at the cozy cure brought off with *Reader's Digest* ease: "The latest democratic dream: not guaranteed annual wages but guaranteed 'success' in bed." But the laughter is too easy. Everywhere in the West men and women by the millions burn, helplessly, within and without marriage, finger themselves off, torment themselves with guilt, belabor each other in silent, killing war—and that which helps them, that which lifts them momentarily beyond the meanness of their losing lives, can't really be despised. The Washington University study didn't aim at improving people's sex lives—but the directors knew that in a neutral setting homely words could be said that might effect change. A sense, in fact, of meanness conquered and ordinary life freshened here and there, surprised by joy, can be made out in the closing pages of the Masters and Johnson report by anyone as yet unfrozen in postures of *de haut en bas*. Doubtless connections exist between this new American fantasy—joyous sex for the masses—and others of the past: salvation through community colleges, salvation through Beethoven LPs. But there is dignity in the fantasy nevertheless, as in all humane egalitarianism, and beauty as well —the beauty of decency, generosity, and hope. With this in mind, and remembering the continuity of the project with intellectual tradition, the idea of abusing the work of Masters and Johnson as sin and deviltry looks cheap.

But those who delivered the abuse *were* provoked to do so—which is to say that, when the full context of the sex-lab war is studied, there's blame for everybody, not just for literary men. If the world of science has a right to be embarrassed for poets who miss the unity of rational inquiry in the immediate past, the world of letters has the right to be embarrassed in turn for scientists who persist in hawking superstitions of the kind implicit in Masters-Johnson chatter about "physiologic truth as opposed to cultural fiction." A major lesson of the sharpest contemporary thought, after all—see Cassirer—stresses the mutuality of mythical and scientific understanding of "fact"; the pretense that "subjective" and "objective" realities can be crisply disentangled by any bright chap with a white coat, a stopwatch, and a mind unviolated by poetry is disingenuous if not dumb. Masters and Johnson learned that there is a sense in which coital and masturbatory orgasms, when compared in strict physiological terms, can be described as "the same." But the manner in which they reported this and a dozen other "challenges to myth" indicated that they had excluded ordinary attitudes and responses, and were persuading themselves that the purely physiological man they posited wasn't a conceptual model or abstraction but a genuine human being. And the literary men who scored off this delusion did indeed have a point.

What is more, the sex researchers look to have been, on balance, a rather fearful lot. A striking portion of their evidence bore on the comparative intensity of male and female sexuality; the evidence suggested the edge belongs to the female. Yet the researchers never faced the findings directly: they trimmed in the presence of them, or shyly turned aside. As might have been expected, fellow professionals called them out for their reticence. Writing in the *Journal of the American Psychoanalytic Association,* Dr. Mary J. Shurfey remarked, on the basis of the Masters-Johnson research, that "to all intents and purposes, *the human female is sexually insatiable in the presence of the highest degrees of sexual satiation,*" and went on not only to draw attention to the possible social consequences of dissemination of findings in this area, but to chide the researchers for their evasiveness and self-censorship.[3]

THE MOST PROVOCATIVE gesture of the sex researchers, however, wasn't finally a matter either of trimming or superstition. It was, instead, the rejection of imaginative flexibility—a gesture that smutched the very ideal of inclusiveness that brought the project to life. Brainy men, serious and earnest men, can indeed stand to know everything, the nineteenth-century idealists had implicitly insisted. Not only can the full truth of human smallness as well as of human nobility be endured, it perhaps can be

[3] Dr. Shurfey commented first on the likeness between the sexual responsivity of the human female and that of certain higher primates: "having no cultural restrictions, these primate females will perform coitus from twenty to fifty times a day during the peak week of estrus usually with several series of copulations in rapid succession. If necessary, they flirt, solicit, present, and stimulate the male in order to obtain successive coitions." After observing that "our myth of the female's relative asexuality is a biological absurdity," she noted that the satiation-in-insatiation state of the primate and human females parallels "the behavior ascribed to women during the prepatriarchal, Mesolithic period—and well into the Neolithic Bronze Age—of history. . . ." Her argument was that womankind's sexuality has been ruthlessly suppressed in the name of monogamy, and in service of a man-centered civilization. Since that suppression seems now to be easing ("a decided lifting of the ancient social injunctions against the free expression of female sexuality has occurred"), the present moment, Dr. Shurfey speculated, could well become one of cultural reorganization:

> . . . one thing is certain: if women's sexual drive has not abated, and they prove incapable of controlling it, thereby jeopardizing family life and child care, a return to the rigid, enforced suppression will be inevitable and mandatory. Otherwise the biological family will disappear and what other patterns of infant care and adult relationships could adequately substitute cannot now be imagined.

Speculation in this vein might have been inappropriate in the Masters-Johnson report. But that report was needlessly inhibited about underscoring findings with direct bearing on central domestic institutions. For a further discussion of Dr. Shurfey's interpretation of these findings, see the *Journal of the American Psychoanalytic Association* for July, 1968.

used for the betterment of this world. And those who use it, the argument ran, will become men of humor, blitheness, unarrogant skepticism. They will learn to take pleasure in their own deflation, they will become even-handed acceptors of the general human humiliation, steady riders, sound hearts. Thomas Mann spelled out the vision once in a famous address on "Freud and the Future," claiming that with the analytic revelation "a blithe skepticism has come into the world, a mistrust that unmasks all schemes and subterfuges of our own souls. Once roused and on the alert, it cannot be put to sleep again. It infiltrates life, undermines its raw naïveté, takes from it the strain of its own ignorance . . . inculcates the taste for understatement . . . for the deflated rather than for the inflated words, for the cult which exerts its influence by moderation, by modesty. Modesty—what a beautiful word!"

But however valuable the Masters-Johnson documents are for the improvement of the national sex life, they don't incarnate this beautiful vision. The problem isn't that the projectors should have acknowledged that, as the literary men charged, the subjects were "making fools of themselves," or were without taste or reticence, or were having their sexual needs catered to far too lavishly. The problem is that, when at length the researchers undertook to deal with the *innerness* of their subjects, they offered up a false account of feelings, one whose omissions were as substantial as any found in the "cultural fiction" against which they inveighed.

Consider the passages about Subject D quoted above. The authors are speaking here, by their own claim, not about physiological reactions but about what it was like, in human terms, to be a subject in this study. Yet their words leave the impression that the entire sequence of feeling can be expressed as a straight-line progression from doggedness to surprise to gratitude. Understandable, perhaps, not to allude directly to courage, desperation, presumed humiliations, frowns of impatience, and self-disgust (as when "coition [was] attempted without ejaculatory success"). Forgivable, owing to the need for sustaining a neutral tone, for the authors to translate the comments of Subject D and his wife into bureaucratese. (Subject D's wife probably didn't *state* that "subsequent to program participation my husband has been infinitely more effective both in stimulating and in satisfying my sexual tensions." And Subject D himself probably did not *say* that "I, in turn, find her wholly responsive without reservation.")

But it is unforgivable, and utterly unscientific, to pass out adman or testimonial simplicities as a substitute for an account of the whole psychological process of improving a sexual relationship—the subtleties and intricacies of self-perception in such a venture, the details of inward change, shadings and redefinitions of trust and confidence, and subsequent characterological transformation. "Together they maintain that they have gotten a great deal more out of cooperation with the program than they have contributed, and they wish to continue on a long-term basis"— as a summary of the emotional and intellectual realities known by human beings in the course of such a project, is this statement not as deceitful as the claim that "there is no such thing as sex"? Was it not unprofessional—not to say "fictional" or "mythical"—to set forth patches of back-patting uplift as a substitute for the full story? How is the ordinary reader—hundreds of thousands of copies of Masters and Johnson have been bought by ordinary readers—to know, given these deeply censored case studies, together with the five years of silence that have followed them, that a full story has been withheld?

AGAIN A CAUTIONARY word is necessary. Asking such questions doesn't mean lining up with the literary anti-sexologist, the critic whose hostility to the scientists' practice of expunging psychological contingencies from the records leads him to vilify sex research as sin. Nor does it mean pretending that the sex researchers included their uplift case studies purely out of pride, and not in the defensive hope of justifying their project and quieting criticism. It does mean asserting that the sex researchers' determination to praise themselves as courageous debunkers was obnoxious, and that the alternative to myth that they have thus far presented isn't much more adequate to truth than the myth itself. They do have certain clear achieve-

ments to their credit. The sex lab proved that, in physiological terms, no significant relation exists between the size
of the penis and coital satisfaction, nor any necessary connection between masturbatory orgasm and "frustration."
The special physiological language it developed can be
helpful to men, and does provide relief from the voguish
porno puerilities of an "age of sexual liberation." Say it
straight out: the laboratory situation creates a possibility
of teaching people *what to do*. If participation by the scientific and literary intellects in each other's accountings of
"facts" were the rule, as it ought to be not only here but
in a dozen other critical areas of contemporary intellectual
inquiry, the "achievement" would rouse more positive feelings than depression.

But as matters stand depression is appropriate. Founded
as yet another venture on behalf of inclusiveness, the sex
lab and attendant controversies testify that, for poet and
methodologist alike, the whole human story is too much to
face up to, too complex, contradictory, dense in variables
to be set out in tight professional vocabularies. We are led
from a valley of deprivation into a valley of abstraction.
We understand that the latter could be furnished, could
be made comfortable for humanness. Sensitive men from
both letters and science—call them scientific humanists—
could do the job, provided they were committed to direct,
patient, collaborative survey of problems, provided they
were prepared to determine in continuous partnership
when and where the methods of detachment can be pro-
ductive, and when and where sympathy with contrarieties
and delicacies of moment-to-moment personal response
must not be foregone. But where are these men? They
haven't come forth as of this moment, and until they appear abstraction rules unchallenged. We are offered no
choice save to avert our eyes from full inward intricacy,
comedy, dignity—full human nakedness—that which the
great thinkers of the relevant past imagined men would
some day learn to relish, not just endure. And our deep
need—stupid ever to make light of it—for a sense of an
ideal possibility, a ground from which sane minds can
feel forward, tentatively, in the direction of a more habit-
able future, continues to go unmet.

The Homecoming Singer

Jay Wright

THE PLANE tilts in to Nashville,
coming over the green lights
like a toy train skipping past
the signals on a track.
The city is livid with lights,
as if the weight of all the people
shooting down her arteries
had inflamed them.
It's Friday night,
and people are home for the homecomings.
As I come into the terminal,
a young black man, in a vested gray suit,
paces in the florid Tennessee air,
breaks into a run like a halfback
in open field, going past the delirious faces,
past the shiny poster of Molly Bee,
in her shiny chaps, her hips tilted forward
where the guns would be, her legs set,
as if she would run, as if she were
a cheerleader who doffs her guns
on Saturday afternoon and careens
down the sidelines after some broken field runner,
who carries it in, for now,
for all the state of Tennessee
with its nut-smelling trees,
its stolid little stone walls
set out under thick blankets of leaves,
its crisp lights dangling on the porches
of homes that top the graveled driveways,
where people who cannot yodel or yell
putter in the grave October afternoons,
waiting for Saturday night and the lights
that spatter on Molly Bee's silver chaps.
I don't want to think of them,
or even of the broken field runner in the terminal,

still looking for his girl, his pocket
full of dates and parties, as I come
into this Friday night of homecomings
and hobble over the highway in a taxi
that has its radio tuned to country music.
I come up to the campus,
with a large wreath jutting up
under the elegant dormitories,
where one girl sits looking down at the shrieking cars,
as the lights go out, one by one, around her
and the laughter drifts off, rising, rising,
as if it would take flight away
from the livid arteries of Nashville.
Now, in sleep, I leave my brass-headed bed,
and see her enter with tall singers,
they in African shirts, she in a robe.
She sits, among them, as a golden lance
catches her, suddenly chubby, with soft lips
and unhurried eyes, quite still in the movement
around her, waiting, as the other voices fade,
as the movement stops, and starts to sing,
her voice moving up from its tart entrance
until it swings as freely
as an ecstatic dancer's foot,
rises and plays among the windows
as it would with angels and falls,
almost visible, to return to her,
and leave her shaking with the tears
I'm ashamed to release, and leave her
twisting there on that stool with my shame
for the livid arteries, the flat Saturdays,
the inhuman homecomings of Nashville.
I kneel before her. She strokes my hair,
as softly as she would a cat's head
and goes on singing, her voice shifting
and bringing up the Carolina calls,
the waterboy, the railroad cutter, the jailed,
the condemned, all that had been forgotten
on this night of homecomings, all
that had been misplaced in those livid arteries.
She finishes, and leaves,
her shy head tilted and wrinkled,
in the green-tinged lights of the still campus.
I close my eyes and listen,
as she goes out to sing this city home.

The End of Days

M. F. Beal

Darrell Hurt was having a hard time sawing through the tough throathide of a steer, though he had butchered more than a hundred in his life as stockman and farmer, when suddenly the white-furred skin split, his knife ripped the jugular, sending a fountain of blood over his hipboots, and he realized he would never be able to finish the butchering.

He dragged himself to one of the hewn timbers of the barn and leaned against it, head hidden in his arm, knife dripping on the floor, eyes cemented shut by a feeling just short of weeping.

It was a large barn that he and his wife and brother Ben had built in '28. The supporting timbers were logs so thick around you could barely embrace them and feel your fingertips; the floor was three-inch, end-grain, old-growth fir with concrete gutters where once he'd milked a dairy herd. The ceiling was twenty-four feet high with a loft holding racked haybales; at the very peak swung a block and tackle with its system of ropes, its singletree to be hooked where hamstring met hock of the hindlegs of the butchered steers. Through the barn doors he had left half-open, the wind tossed dime-sized drops of winter rain.

Darrell tried to understand why he could not finish the butchering. His eyes were drawn to the animal's blood as it pattered the flooring, found cracks, and sought the earth below. The yarddog, Sam, left his treat of a severed hoof to lap the flow; feeling Darrell's eyes, he flagged a long tailswing, flattened his ears as he wolfishly continued. The smell of the steer, heavy with softness, grain, and the yellowness of warm fat from the steer's brisket and back, reached Darrell in wind gusts, then dragged off, up through the hay, down to the richening loam beneath the barn. Where he had skinned the belly (before the inertia set in) and cut away the long brown tasseled organ of the steer, the fat stood clumped, erect. And though he knew quite well the steer was dead of a bullet aimed downward behind the ear into the mass of its brain, he could see that when the wind touched the skinned ribs of the creature, its muscles rippled, remembering how to dislodge a fly. *It is still alive*, he thought suddenly, but he knew it was not.

He jabbed his knife into a beam with a quick snap of wrist and reached into the bucket of warm water he always had at the butchering. He rubbed his hands as if he wished he were soaping them; then, with this familiarity in his head, he told his feet to move to the next step: lifting the steer onto the singletree hoist. But they would not move. *I will have to go up to the house for awhile, till this passes*, he decided.

THERE WAS A RISING PATH leading to the house set into the top of the hill. The house was of concrete blocks; Darrell had only finished it three winters before. Sometimes when he thought of all the years he and Verna and Sally had lived in what was now the wood and tool shed, he had to stop and shake his head before he could pick up the screwdriver or hammer or stick of wood he was after.

He walked up the rising path slowly and watched the outlines of the house come clear through the rain. There were lights in the windows. A man who had stopped the summer before to ask permission to fish from their bridge said the house reminded him, somehow, of the old houses —shelters—the first settlers had built on the Great Plains. Darrell liked the idea of that; he told the man he was one of the early settlers in this part of the West. No man had farmed this land before. It had been burned-over stumpland, the trees fired by the Indians so grass would grow up and give more graze for deer and elk. Then the government opened it for settlement, and some crazy old man took papers on it, built a tiny shack—even smaller than

Darrell's—down by the creek, and sat there and read books
till he died. Darrell bought the land from the old guy's
cousin, paid the place off working on the highway crew
and logging, and now, forty-one years after getting it, after
yarding out stumps, plowing, seeding, fencing and stock-
ing, had almost a hundred acres of prime bottom pasture,
pure-bred Hereford beefcritters, the new concrete block
house.

Verna was working in the kitchen. She looked up as he
undid his boots, dropped them on the mat.

"Finish the butchering? I've got something here you
sure will hate to see." Her voice told him she'd baked a pie
or some such treat. He gained weight now that he was
getting older and she didn't bake pies for him as often.

"Whatcha got? Let's see—from the smell in here I'd say
it's something pretty bad. Did you burn some grease . . .
no, it's worse than that." He chuckled like crumpling
paper.

"Oh, Darrell, I baked you an apple pie." She opened
the oven door to show it. He couldn't get over how tired
he felt, how the sight of the pie seemed suddenly to fist
his stomach into a tight sour lump.

"I'm feeling a little under the weather," he said. Knowing that already, she looked up from pouring milk into a
pitcher. A drop of milk fell on her apron; the fabric swallowed it. "I think I'll lie down," he said.

THE LIVINGROOM was twenty-six by thirty-two. They
had wanted a big livingroom and that size seemed about
right. But now that the house was built, he was appalled
each time he entered the room at just how enormous
twenty-six by thirty-two was. Inside the room with its
high ceiling and double windows, he felt somehow out of
scale; as if he had grown smaller. Staring out the windows
into the pastured valley he now and then was amazed to
think himself a deep-sea diver; the plumed and fronded
trees swayed with currents and pressures greater than any
he had imagined and his eyes warily sought the warning
fin of some incredible fish come to stare back. Inside this
room, he could feel the weight of that different atmos-

phere on his shoulders, inside his head. "Like a fish out of water," he'd think to himself, the idea flowing into his head as the trees bent to the wind. But that wasn't it, exactly; he meant almost the direct opposite. Still, that was what came to mind. That these were the only words to express what he felt disturbed him, too; it made him think things inside him were folding and bending like the world outside his window. How could you admit you couldn't sometimes tell grass from water? You couldn't tolerate things going unreal like that. Yet they did, and there were moments of panic like this afternoon in the barn when you almost thought you wanted them to.

He eased into his chair and stared at the carpet, a long, thick one that swirled into patterns as you walked through it; it was green, like his pastures, but as seen underwater. "How's that for grass?" he found himself asking each new visitor in an almost worried attempt to recover, simply, what it *must* be. But they always agreed, saying: "Best looking crop of grass I ever seen."

Verna called his chair "the cradle." It was an arc of beige moire plastic pushed into soft tufted swells. He did not sit in it but lay down, knees and head slightly raised. Under the right armrest was a switch and when he pressed it, the chair began to vibrate gently. It helped his back; it relaxed away the knot in his belly. It was hard to stay awake when the switch was on.

But even as his finger touched the switch, he noticed on the little table beside him the card they'd been given at the funeral of the Disston boy.

HE AND VERNA had had a boy. They had Sally, and then four years later Verna got pregnant again. Everyone joked about this one being another girl, but Darrell's father —who was alive then—said "No, by god, this one's going to have a handle on 'im." Darrell's mother had borne seven children and his father had infallibly predicted the sex of each. Well, when Verna's baby was born it was a son, all right, but it lacked calcium in its bones, the doctor said, and so when it got out of its mother it just seemed to collapse inward, a creature out of its element. The doctor said it was a rare case, that he wanted to write it up for some journal. Darrell signed papers giving permission; and then a few years later began to dream at night his son was in a bottle somewhere on some laboratory shelf, still a prisoner *inside*. But now inside glass, a prison of glass and alcohol. After her confinement, Verna never spoke of the baby at all.

The death of the neighbor's son had been, in a sense, expected. When they were told Bobby Disston had been hit and killed by a car while he was changing a tire on the roadside in the dusk everyone was shocked, but the next response was: I always suspected something would happen to that kid. He was always getting into scrapes, and had had several minor accidents. "He used his life as if all he had to do was walk into the dimestore and buy a new one," another neighbor said. Even his mother said, "I knew it. I knew it."

The funeral announcement showed a chapel window with pink and yellow shafts filtering through on a cross; it was on thin crisp paper. On the inside was a poem:

> To close the eye, to fall asleep,
> To draw a labored breath,
> To find release from daily cares
> In what we know as death . . .
>
> Is this the crowning of a life,
> The aim or end thereof?
> The totaled sum of consciousness,
> The ripened fruit of love?
>
> It cannot be, for they live on
> A little step away.
> The soul, the everlasting life,
> Has found a better day . . .

Darrell did and didn't believe any of it. He did believe the poem; he didn't believe Bobby Disston had been *headed* for a bad end. But during and after the funeral he realized something: they, all of them in the world, when such things happened, were nearing the end of days;

and it was not long off now. The Last Judgment was near. He had not spoken to anyone yet of this.

HIS FINGERS TOUCHED THE BUTTON on the underside of the chairarm. With the card in his other hand he dozed and dreamt:

He was standing outside the funeral home; there was a funeral, and he had been invited. He had on his best suit, a dark blue one; he rubbed the tip of one shoe on the back of his trouserleg, then the other. He thought: this doesn't make sense; I haven't done that since I was a kid. There was difficulty getting someone to answer the door. He rang again and again; he could hear inside the music of the service, but no one answered the door. I'm late, he thought. They've gone on without me. He realized his hair was out of place and tried to smooth it with his hand, but his hair was stiff, hard like animal hair, and would not lie flat. He yanked his hand away in panic, pushed at the door.

Now suddenly the funeral director appeared and though they were men of the same age and even had fished together, the director didn't greet him; he said nothing, in fact, though Darrell spoke to him somberly about being late, and how sorry he was, and what a tragedy about Bobby Disston. Instead the director hustled—literally shoved—him into a tiny room. It was dark, a closet. He could hear the music, then the voice of the preacher, but couldn't make out the words. The room, which had seemed so tiny at first, expanded but remained dark; then it contracted, was even smaller than at first. He couldn't stand; he lay down. He stretched out his feet. The music had stopped now; even the preacher's voice was fading and instead he heard a roar, a dull heavy sound of water moving, pressing. He tried to struggle up, to stand again. He could not.

VERNA CALLED DARRELL'S BROTHER BEN to help finish the butchering and after supper the men started down the path to the barn. It was getting dark and Darrell had turned on the floodlight. He couldn't get over how much the trees were like feathers. Darrell felt he had never seen trees before. "Trees, grass—they're alive," he thought, unable to be more precise about his new idea than that, but contented with the notion.

Ben talked about how the Grange needed a new roof. "I've stuck them damn shingles down till there's nothing left of 'em but roofing tar." It was true; Darrell nodded. "I'm going into Portland next week; I'll price them. Eleanor says burn the place down and start right; but I think a new roof will do 'er."

"I was skinning and I got a little light feeling, you know?" Darrell said while his head was clear. They had reached the barn. The steer lay belly up on the floor and its flanks no longer quivered when the wind struck muscle. Its belly was enormous, reaching almost to the midleg knuckle where Darrell had sawed off the hooves, the first task of butchering. Sam flopped his tail at them and continued to chew one of the discarded feet. And Darrell thought another of his unwelcome thoughts: for all the doctors' skill in putting one man's heart into another man, or sewing in new kidneys, some things were beyond all resurrection.

"It's funny how weak I feel when I get down here in the wind," he said.

"There's a flu going around," said Ben, working a flap of hide down, fleshing away with the sharp knife. The fat under the steer's hide was white and where the capillaries to the hide had been severed, there were tiny dribbles of red, as if it had been flailed with the thorns of the running blackberry that hedged the pastures.

"Better get that blood off before it sets," Darrell said. He fixed his jaw and found he could take up the garden-hose to run jets of water on the fat, found even he could put his hand on the fat and scrub a bit to loosen the red. The steer had a different smell now, a strong thick one that fought into the nostrils even though Darrell breathed through his mouth. He heard Ben doing the same, both of them panting.

"Stiffening up now," said Ben. "Better get this damn hide off."

Darrell took up a knife then, and worked the hide with his brother.

Soon Ben was hooking the hocks to the singletree and Darrell, pulling at the block and tackle, had the hindquarters off the floor. His hands trembled as he sliced the brisket, through the heavy fat, to the ribs. Ben urged the tip of his knife under the muscle at the belly, nudging the tip in small jerks to penetrate muscle but not intestine. The fascia popped, hissed like a kid's balloon. Intestine bulged through the parting.

"Lots of gas," said Ben. There was a new odor now, a green slime smell of decay. The floodlight had become their only illumination and under it the fat sides of the critter as they parted buckled into dimples and swells, grew yellow-pink, waxy, mottled like the thighs of a fat old woman. Darrell saw fat and muscle cling to each other before this last dismemberment. He had always thought change natural before; now he suddenly saw the resistance even a dead thing could make. Then was it "natural" for one thing to be changed into another, as he and Verna might consume steak? Was it "natural" (the arithmetic leapt into his head) that in his sixty-five years almost thirty steers like this one had passed through him, that almost ten tons of critter had gone to nourish his two hundred pounds? If it happened, well then it must. Or? The intestines popped angrily from the cavity as Ben worked his incision to the clumps of fat where the steer's member had been. Pressing them back with his hands, feeling the veins of his hands and wrists knot to press, Darrell stood, feet spread, wondering whether to tell Ben they were in the end of days.

How would he say it? *The wars, the killings, young men dying, old men without energy; fighting, killing for no good reason, accidents . . . it used to happen, it all happened before but never this way, never so many, with so little sense.* And of course it was written, as well. *The prophets saw, they told us, they gave us a blueprint. How long do we have? A year? A hundred days?* It could happen tomorrow.

The lungs and stomach finally bulged out now, slipped between Darrell's hands, slapped the floor. Ben panted, stepped back, wiped his forehead, looked at Darrell, waiting. For what? There was a quizzical look in Ben's eyes. Finally Darrell saw, moved to the block and tackle, cranked the steer higher.

"You want the tail, Darrell?"

"No."

Ben found the joint, cut; the tail fell. Darrell cut a hank of twine, slid it around the tight colon as Ben held the guts aside, and cinched it up.

They began to search the entrails for the liver: Darrell, slipping again into the job, called to the dog who trotted up, took a lunglobe with careful teeth, backed off.

"Want the sweetbreads, Darrell?"

"No."

"You got the heart there? I'll take the hanging tender."

Cutting away the heart and the shaft of muscle that held it in place, Darrell answered himself: *no, I won't say anything, no one will know.* He gripped the colon and pulled back. Ben grunted, ran his knife around the anus; there was a suck of air, the guts splayed on the floor, gleamed. The dog clicked his teeth.

And how tired Darrell was now; he himself felt flayed, taken apart. The heart lay in its bucket with the tender coiled around it; he drew kidneys from the gaping chest, sent them to rest on the heart. So much to do: hide to fist from the back, head to sever, carcass to wash again with cloths . . .

"Not much left now, Darrell," said Ben looking at him again, with that queer look. And suddenly Darrell realized what Ben saw: Darrell dying. Darrell old, tired, speechless, afraid. And when the end of days had come for him, Darrell, Ben would say: "I knew he wasn't long for this world. I could see it that night."

Verna—could she see it? Would she say "I knew it, I knew it"? Would they sit in the funeral home, in the chapel that was not really like the pink-yellow lit chapel on the card; the real chapel, and in the sanctuary, a real, vast, dark casket enclosing himself, who was really dead? Would they go *on*?

No Last Judgment, no end of days. They would go on. The huge livingroom of his new stone house would be no more or less empty. "Old Darrell died, did you hear about it?" "Is that a fact; well to tell you the truth I saw it coming."

He found himself giving Ben a look of pure hate and his brother, alarmed, took his shoulder.

"Darrell, you look bad. You go up to the house."

AND AS HIS FEET LIFTED him up the dark path his body seethed. His face filled, his chest, his ribs lifted to hard bundles. He felt his organs had been turned to stone; his body, stiff, drum-tight, seethed and burned; molten, furious. *I want them all to come with me,* his head shouted: *I want to kill them all, kill them all, all——*

Viewing the Body

S. S. Gardons

Flowers like a gangster's funeral;
  Eyeshadow like a whore.
They all say isn't she beautiful.
  She, who never wore

Lipstick or such a dress,
  Never got taken out,
Was scarcely looked at, much less
  Wanted or talked about;

Who, gray as a mouse, crept
  The dark halls at her mother's
Or snuggled, soft, and slept
  Alone in the dim bedcovers.

Today at last she holds
  All eyes and a place of honor
Till the obscene red folds
  Of satin close down on her.

Two Poems

David P. Young

Poem for Wrists

WRISTS! I want to
write you a poem you
whom nurses finger watches
circle razors open
handcuffs chill—you are
taken for granted wrists!
therefore assert yourselves
take charge of your
unruly friends the hands
keep them from triggers, off
necks give them a light
touch have them wave bye-bye
teach them to let
go at the right moment oh
wrists shy ankles of the arm
on whom farms flyrods
shovels whips and poems
so naturally depend.

The Boxcar Poem

THE BOXCARS drift by
clanking
they have their own
speech on scored

wood their own
calligraphy
Soo Line
they say in meadows
Lackawanna quick at crossings
Northern Pacific, a
nightmurmur, Northern
Pacific

even empty
they carry
in dark corners
among smells of wood and sacking
the brown wrappings of sorrow
the rank straw of revolution
the persistence of war

and often
as they roll past
like weathered obedient
angels you can see
right through them
to yourself
in a bright
field, a crow
on either shoulder.

The Cinderella Kid

Henry H. Roth

How much do you want to know?

Better, how much do I want to know or tell?

I grew up with colored and Spanish kids. All were in the same lousy boat and I saw right away most kids stink and those that are brave and smart keep their mouths shut and noses clean and hope for some guy or lady with a magic stick to get you out of the Home. Believe me it was no real home but a Home for Orphans; you never forgot how you owed everything to the Sisters, the social workers, and all citizens who paid taxes. There was a kid in my cottage whose old man was killed robbing a bank. Well, as he grew up his only aim in life was to be a bank robber. I mean that's all the past history he knew, so he grabbed that. He was so sad I don't know if I wanted him to make it or not.

As for me I had no memory of parents, so I picked out what was going on right now that I could understand which was sports. I knew the world didn't give a shit about me and if I made a mistake they would put me in worse places than the Home so I was goody goody until it became a habit. While my buddies got into more trouble as they got older I stayed clean but no one called me chicken shit because I was real big and strong. The joke is that the kids didn't really see they were different from other kids, while I knew I was just pretending to be a human being.

I pretended so long that I got lucky, very lucky for a while. Like the little guys at the Home who prayed each day they might get adopted or somehow their parents would show up in big cars and drive them away to a fancy house, I also dreamed. It was some lumpy shape waving something. It wasn't scary though; it was like the kind witch in the *Wizard of Oz*, or sometimes it was a man like a prince—shit I never told anyone, they would've put me away. But when my luck came and they nicknamed me The Cinderella Kid at the training camp in Florida I wasn't surprised. For a while I was The Cinderella Kid.

The only way I could get off of the Home grounds was sports. So I went out for everything. I played a lot of basketball and football but it was boring. Baseball was my game right away. It couldn't begin or end without me because I was the star pitcher, a real king of any hill. My arm was my golden button to everything. By my junior year in high school scouts were calling up my cottage or asking to speak to the chief administrator. Coach Sutton always treated me like a person, not like some freak who could do one thing great. He handled the negotiations. Everyone in town started noticing and singling me out. The Home girls are ready to screw from twelve on; it was about the only exciting thing we had to do there. But now the town girls were saying hello, I was like the star quarterback of a high school I never went to. After twelve nohitters, I was even invited to the mayor's house. At the end of my senior year with plenty of local publicity I signed for twenty-five thousand dollars, payment to be spread over five years.

MOST OF THE diary I kept the first February in Florida is gone but I still keep the few pages left near my draft card and birth certificate:

. . . first day in Florida. It's fucking cold. I share a room with one guy, *one guy*. All the hot water and food you can ask for. Curfu is ten o'clock. Don't worry I'm not going to screw up here.

. . . when I finish batting practice some coach walked over pated my head and arm and said not to throw so hard tomorrow. Just like Coach Sutton but this is the majors.

. . . my roomie is a pitcher too, he's been looking at me real funny. He should I'm faster and only throw strikes . . . some reglars on the team had supper with me . . . I didn't say a fucking word just like when I was at the mayer's house.

. . . last night I walked round the beach barefoot kicking sand into the Atlantic. My best dream was never one million as swell as whats happening. Pitch three innings tomorrow.

. . . two hits no runs no walks six strikeouts. My roomie caught a cold. Tough.

. . . wrote Coach Sutton this morning. Took a dip in the pool for the first time. First time someone didn't tell me when to come out of the pool. Pitch again Friday.

. . . my buddy was sent to the farm team camp. I don't mind his empty bed I've never been in a room alone. Four innings today three hits no runs two walks four strikeouts. A writer did a whole artacel on me. Last night I woke up crying, glad that prick wasn't there. He had a teriffic control problem.

. . . club still carrying plenty of guys over the limit but I'm still one of them. One coach is my pal, even if it's bullshit I like it. Wish I knew how to talk better but I don't want them to laff at me. Some wise guy said I'm not any Cinderella Kid but the Humbel kid. Some day I'll put him down with a better knickname meantime I brushed him in batting practice.

. . . we're out of Florida and the veterans say it wasn't as good wether as other years. Nuts, it was paradize. From now on we go 6 innings each start . . . hell I can go 66 innings. My new roomie is a catcher rookie like me and we go over all the hitters. Imagen talking about how to get Willie Mays out, it's so crazy like figring how to screw Kim Novak. I mean anything is possible.

. . . supposed to go seven today. Charlott last stop. next the big City. My roomie split a finger he's really wurryed they won't carry him now.

During my first trip north, I had pitched so good I was still with the varsity. Look I was a big strong wiseassed kid who wanted everything right away. Charlotte was the next to last game before opening day; I felt tight warming up but I knew it would loosen up. But it didn't. I was very wild, lucky to last the first two innings; I walked three in the first, two in the second. Manager was giving smug fishy looks. He didn't say anything but I could see our bullpen warming up. My arm felt lead heavy, the ball was like a snowball I couldn't really grip. I was scared and mad. There was no chatter from the infield, everyone was waiting for me to fold, to blow sky high. I walked the first batter in the third then I shook off my catcher when he signaled a fastball, and again shook him off for a curve and nodded for a slider. Christ the catcher was pissed. Also I forgot to hold the runner and went into a full windup. "Steal," the second baseman yelled. In the middle of my motion I caught myself and aimed the ball to the plate real fast. A line drive right to the third baseman who had an easy doubleplay. By the time I got back to the dugout I was trying not to cry. I'll never forget that bush fire running through my shoulder into my hand and killing my fingers. I couldn't believe anything could hurt like that and I kept looking at my arm. I couldn't believe it was still there.

In time the arm got stronger but when it came to pitching I was feeble after ten minutes of lobbing batting practice. I had to throw three quarters and there was no sign of any fast ball, the ball headed toward the plate with little or no spin. From Charlotte they sent me down to Tennessee, where I would faithfully warm up each day, toss the glove high into the air, then crouch in the smelly dugout. Most nights I would end up on the grass half drunk, listening to a pretty little river that split the town's main street and led nowhere and served no purpose except to calm me down.

That was my whole summer, dressing but not playing anymore. And me only eighteen. Labor Day, my joke season finished, I went back home. Another bad joke. The Home was a real home for losers. I returned because there was nowhere else to go. I still had my car and no one could take away the bonus, but my arm, my rocket to other worlds, was out of fuel. Coach Sutton let me help him in football, basketball, and wrestling, and then it was time for another spring training.

That season I was in three towns. They kept sending me around, hoping that sun and dry air might heal the muscles. I only got hotter and drier and the desert towns were like jails; the arm hurt so bad I really began to have a real drinking problem; it was all I could manage by myself. There was no future for me; if not for the bonus I would be pumping gas at a nearby Esso but even with money what else was I qualified to handle? Coach Sutton suggested I try college, our community college accepted anybody with a high school diploma which I did have. The final push was a form letter from the ball club stating that *my contractual obligation for the next three years would entail only showing up for spring training and determining whether there had been any significant improvement in my condition.*

THE PARKING LOT at the Community College could have been for an A & P except there were plenty of trees plus instructions all over the place. Area reserved for faculty —reserved for maintenance—reserved for students—no parking any time. Wow, I should have left my car on the damn grass because I sure didn't belong there. The guidance man looked like he agreed except it was his job not to agree and I did have a high school diploma.

"We wish to help you," he said, "we've begun a Seek program to help the dis. . . ."

I knew that word. "Disadvantaged, you mean." Boy was he ever right. Yet he was a nice guy, really turned on, really interested.

"Eddie Sutton has spoken to me."

"He's a great guy."

After a while the guidance man sucked on his pipe and said, "You know, you're a very interesting and determined young man."

I wish I hadn't answered. "And scared."

That he really liked—a scared disadvantaged.

"You speak very well," he said.

I wanted to smash him, shout at him, yell so fucking loud he'd fall right off his swivel chair, the bastard. But he was nice. So far it's taken me twenty years to speak at all. I never talked much at the Home but not because I was shy or had nothing to say. I just wasn't going to growl and curse like those other apes. So I kept quiet like some of those monks, and I watched TV news and all the broadcasters, Brinkley, Huntley, Cronkite. I watched them everyday. I didn't understand much of what they said, but I saw how they paused a lot even sighed and they never said well or uh before talking. And they never cursed. I tried to copy them and still do. I knew my vocabulary wasn't much but Coach Sutton explained I would begin slowly at college and get special classes and help. Most important, he promised nobody would make me feel small.

"I can tell you're a very mature young man."

I flapped my dead arm. "I was a pitcher."

"Mr. Sutton told me. Very unfortunate. But I'm glad you're here. Our program is just beginning. We must both be patient."

He sounded like a pitching coach, only he smiled all the time. And then a girl came in who he introduced as my new coach. The greatest looking girl who shook my hand and led me to the library. And I have tried real hard to never let that hand get away.

I'll TRY TO report one of our recent conversations. I was packing my suitcase to go South again for spring training.

"You would have never come here if you hadn't . . ."

"Yes m'am, without a sore arm I'd be with nifty women and cars. The sweetlife."

She smiled so much better than any guidance man who ever lived and she's been smiling that way for three years.

"You know that song at the concert, 'Who Am I?'"

Now she began to look sad.

"Look, I'm happy I don't know who I am. I am un-tapped, I am one of the untapped . . ."

"Don't joke."

"I'm not. After I hurt my arm I was drinking a lot. Then one day I remembered Benito who was growing up to be a bank robber like his old man. Coach Sutton was all over me about college and once I got to thinking about Benito, man I almost ran to the school in the middle of the night."

"I hate baseball."

"And I hate the word potential but I love untapped, like there's no end to it or me. If you win thirty games like McLain, that should be the end. He'd be better off to play the organ for the rest of his life."

"I don't understand baseball, you never talk about it."

"You don't want to hear."

"Unless you want me to."

"It's just another bad symbol of America."

"You're not even packing a glove."

I smiled. "You don't want me to."

"It's crazy. You're crazy."

"I'll tell you what baseball is, okay? The guy that can make all the routine chances sticks. Hard chances even the great stars only make less than fifty percent of the time. It's all in the stats. All you have to be is a machine, not messing up the usual everyday bounce."

She was looking straight at me now, neither happy nor sad.

"Till now I haven't ever had one routine chance and I'm not a star so every possible play stays that way. All the other kids at the Home are the same, we get no routine shots—we're all untapped. That sounds like school bullshit but it's true. Really."

"Who are you?" she joked.

The suitcase was locked up.

"If I die," I answered, "I leave my mind to you and my body to baseball."

WHEN I GOT my twenty-five thousand, there were hundreds of other bonus babies all over the country, but I was the only orphan and was promptly nicknamed The Cinderella Kid. Five years later, I'm not worth a fillin note on a lousy rainy Florida day when there are not even any injuries or trade rumors to report. You know there was a writer who did an article on a ballplayer, once called a phenom, who had hung on as 25th man. Now at thirty he was about to be cut. The column was really good, so the local papers reprinted it in each town

the club played on the exhibition schedule. This ballplayer read the same story every day for two weeks;
finally he cornered the writer threatening his life if he
wrote that fucking story one more day. But I wouldn't
get any such goodbyes. I hurt my arm so quickly that
there's no possible interest five years later.

The management was of course furious, annoyed and
tired of me. So for this last tryout I was assigned minor
league quarters for the first time down there. I refused to
report. The travel secretary screamed but each year I'm
one of the protected players so they shouldn't try to deal
that way with me. "It's the last damn year," he muttered
but my accommodations were changed. I know they fired
the scout who signed me, but he hooked on with another
team right away. Hell when he first saw me I was worth
every penny. The bastards didn't even give me a locker
or uniform, still I didn't even bring my glove this year.

I called Janet every other day and wrote her daily, telling her about the book I was reading. Maybe she'd just
found a dumb stud and was developing his mind but I
didn't care. In the words of Lou Gehrig I consider myself
the luckiest man on the face of the earth. Sometimes I
think authors of books are talking only to me, telling me
all their secrets. Words are magic, the rest is a game.
Janet says I may turn out to be a writer. My chances of
that are about as good winning one game in the low
minors. But I will be a teacher. You know I can't wait to
teach at the Home.

THE RAIN FINALLY STOPPED and I'd gotten me a
baggy uniform. Then the best thing happened. Jocko
Gordon was down here. He was my manager the first year
and the only guy I met who really loves the Game; he was
still in the kid league, still happy to be seeing a ball game
every summer day. Jocko greeted me like a long lost son.

"Let's toss a few. Orders," he chuckled. "Toss me one
or two and tell me what you've been doing. You look
great kid."

I didn't toss any but told him my story. That grand old
guy hugged me.

A clean white ball skimmed toward us, I slapped it into
the stiff borrowed glove. "Let's go to work old man."

"Go right ahead."

I shut my eyes, raised my leg, kicked off, and threw straight and easy. The sun was really shining as if saying forgive me for the past few days. Boy what a warm mother sun. Sweat was rolling off my face and I felt powerful and very loose. I was having a real good time and I threw the ball back as soon as it was returned to me by the crouching Jocko. As usual the pitches were slow, straight as strings.

"You don't throw sidearm anymore?"

"You're kidding, I still do."

"You haven't been kid." His voice was funny.

I threw again, he was right, that god damn Jocko was right. It was five years ago, the old smooth-styled delivery.

"Try a curve," he shouted.

I did.

"Hurt?"

"No."

"Snap it off harder this time, don't be scared."

The ball rose then dipped as if shot.

He couldn't handle the pitch and retrieved it on his hands and knees. "I'll be damned I'll be damned," he muttered.

A bat boy came over to us. "Jocko, someone wants to seeya."

"Later."

"C'mon Jocko they're waiting."

"You better go. I'll be here. Don't get our front office mad."

Jocko backed away, eyeing me very funny.

Meanwhile I did a few windsprints, I wasn't in bad shape and right now I felt giddy and light and stupid. This practice field banks down to the back of a high school. I still had the ball in my pants pocket, I slid down the hill and suddenly was all alone. There were trees bunched together. I aimed for the middle broadest one, throwing hard as I could. The effort and the pain that immediately followed sunk me to my knees. Meanwhile the ball was ricochetting back. In my dizzy state I thought the tree had been bent back. And the pain was gone as quickly as it had arrived. I threw again, the tree definitely shuddered. There was no pain at all. The ball banged halfway back and I ran to greet it.

I got back unnoticed, did some more windsprints, and then headed for the clubhouse. I avoided Jocko until supper when he joined me.

"How are ya?"

"Fine Jocko, just fine."

But Jocko was mean and serious.

"I'd like to catch ya again tomorrow. Okay?"

"Sure." I was still smiling.

He tried to match me but he couldn't. "I've been bounced."

"You're kidding?"

"They gave me a scouting job."

"Those bastards."

"The league may fold, they're getting tired carrying young kids and old men."

"I thought that was baseball."

"Look they cudda cut me off completely."

"Wonderful."

"I gotta tellya something else."

"Shoot."

"I followed ya."

"Huh?"

"I was up on the hill watching, my eyes are still very good kid."

"Well . . . ?"

"See ya tomorrow morning. Get a good night's sleep."

Jᴏᴄᴋᴏ ᴀs ʜᴇ ᴘʀᴏᴍɪsᴇᴅ was waiting. He crouched and my heart went out to him, I thought his body would break in two. This was no position for a man close to sixty. He took his cap off; it was crazy how his few hairs pointed up to the sun—an old ball hawk who still loved to sweat.

As for me, I felt like a stranger living on somebody's credit card. I was a one-in-a-million look-a-like for someone else. I was the twin of a dumb strong kid in one of those John Tunis novels making a comeback from a crippling arm injury. I looked at the number one worshiper of false idols, and told Jocko I accept all legends—Hornsby never went to the movies and hated every pitcher, Rabbit Maranville ate goldfish, Ty Cobb was mean, and Walter Johnson never cured. But hell no, Jocko, I won't go. And it's not the generation gap. For I go even further back to the short pieces of O'Henry, not fashionable now, old Jocko, but very big a long time ago. And I take coaching from him.

When I looked again a faceless guy with a tiny glove was going to try and catch me. Balls! So I knocked Jocko flat with a live rising fastball. He took a long time getting up. He was definitely excited. I waited in vain to spy happiness and understanding; there was only greed and lust. He was a company man no matter how much the Company screwed him. Next I gave him the full windup and knuckle balled. Then I flipped another toward him; the ball made it in one nutty bounce. Jocko walked toward me.

"C'mon, kid, stop fooling around."

I've heard that voice most of my life. From impatient social workers, teachers, bored cops, even my own inner voice. But that life style is no more. Jocko is not my man. My spiked cleats are pinching. I point to the right arm. "I should have told you yesterday I can throw real hard once or twice a day, then it's bad as before. I shouldn't have teased."

Jocko wasn't buying. "Let's try some more."

One of the coaches walked over, he hated me because I would never be any use to him. He hated Jocko because Jocko could get *his* job one day. And right now he was bored and boss.

"Okay, kid," he joked, "let's see the high hard one that cost us twenty-five big ones."

I blew kisses at my enemy, grunted, and made it to Jocko on two big bounces.

The man laughed a while. "Jeez, Jocko, can't you find a better way to goof off?"

Jocko was about to say fuck you to one of us. But true baseball man, hypocrite, he just chewed his gum.

Before I left the field and before I left Florida, I returned to my victory scene. There might be spies in the trees, so wisely I carried no baseball. I did pace off sixty feet six inches and I did pitch one classic of a game. A few fouls but that was all. I was carried off the field by my proud teammates; with their cheers and the papers proving my worth I felt neither guilty nor sad calling an airline and arranging a flight. Hell The Cinderella Kid had made it all the way back, you couldn't ask for more than that.

Correspondence

To the Editor:

Many radicals are convinced that it is impossible to express radical ideas in any but radical publications, that an alien context inevitably vitiates those ideas. I have always resisted this position because I want to reach a wider audience than a few thousand faithful. I still feel that way, but after reading *NAR*'s introductory comments on my piece about Chicago (#6), I can see that this philosophy is more safely applied to *Life* or the *Daily News* than to liberal intellectual journals. Only an l.i.j. could have done such a good job of misrepresentation-by-context. That it was clearly unintentional, in a way just makes it worse. As I remarked in my article, it is deflating always to be absorbed rather than attacked.

The key sentence in the introduction is "For libertarianism today runs the gamut from the reasoned social thought of a Paul Goodman or Herbert Marcuse to the 'sluttish antinomianism,' to use George Orwell's phrase, of the Jerry Rubins and Mark Rudds." The same paragraph cites my criticism of the Chicago demonstration. The implication is that along with *NAR* I am on the side of "reasoned social thought" in the battle against "sluttish antinomianism," whatever that is. Uh-uh. Politically and temperamentally Jerry Rubin and I are very far apart, but to me Rubin is still a revolutionary, George Orwell is still a fink, and *NAR* is guilty of a fixation on the written word. In Chicago, Rubin's brilliant handling of the mass media made possible the vivid communication of ideas, emotions, and action to millions of people, something no literary intellectual could have accomplished. What bothered me about the street-fighting in Chicago was not that we weren't all home writing nice reasonable books about Marxism, but that we were betraying class biases. Liberal intellectuals are equally guilty of these biases, and so is Herbert Marcuse, the most influential exponent of the idea that the working class is hopelessly reactionary. The difference is that they express themselves more genteelly. And if there is anything worse than class bias at this time of crisis, it's gentility. In any case, my commitment is not to "libertarianism"—a category of "reasoned social thought" —but to liberation, a condition to be attained through *action*, without which thought means nothing.

It is also misleading to sum up my reaction to Chicago as "we must find a better way than the provocation and the putdown." This vocabulary is *NAR*'s, not mine. As far as I am concerned, the provocation came from Mayor Daley. As for the "putdown," it depends on who or what is being put down. To put down Daley and the Democratic power structure was crucial; to put down the cops, a diversion from the real issue. As I hope I made clear, I took part in the Chicago confrontation because I felt it to be right and necessary, though as it unfolded it revealed its limitations and our shortcomings.

Finally, one comment on the "literate young minds" *NAR* is pleased to publish. For many of us who happen to be literate—we just growed that way—this faculty is as much a burden as an asset. We have a saying: "Good writing is counterrevolutionary." It is a reminder that literature is basically an activity of mandarins; that it is all too easy for a writer to start thinking like a mandarin; that literary mandarins will be eager to recruit us, since there are too few good writers around. It is an exhortation not to glory in literacy as an end in itself, but to use it responsibly. And by "responsibility" I don't mean judiciousness, intellectual respectability or the balanced view. I mean responsibility to our fellows and our struggle.

Ellen Willis

New York City

M. F. Beal's story "Survival" appeared in *NAR* #3. She writes from Seal Rock, Oregon, that "My husband [the novelist David Shetzline] and I are the only people I've heard of writing about the Revolution from the heart of one of the few wildernesses the country still possesses. . . ."

Wm Brown has worked as a photographer, detective, and free-lance editor. His translations of Bonnefoy and J. Dupin appear in *Contemporary French Poetry* and his own poems have been published by *Tri-Quarterly, Jeopardy,* and other little magazines.

Frederick Busch studied at Muhlenberg and Columbia and presently teaches at Colgate. His fiction has appeared in *Vortex, Transatlantic Review,* and *NAR* #5. He has recently completed a novel and is looking for a publisher.

Robert Chatain has been a roofer, draftsman, and soldier since graduating from Columbia in 1965. "The Adventure of the Mantises" is his first published story.

Benjamin DeMott writes for a wide range of periodicals on literary and cultural matters. His second novel, *A Married Man,* was published last year by Harcourt, Brace & World, which will also be bringing out *Supergrow,* Mr. DeMott's latest collection of essays, this fall.

Rosalyn Drexler is best known for her underground musical comedy *Home Movies.* She is at present readying her latest one, *The Line of Least Existence,* for a Broadway production this fall. "Like . . ." is the opening section of her novel *To Smithereens* which World will soon publish.

Richard Eberhart's latest book of poetry is *Shifts of Being.* Mr. Eberhart has been awarded the 1969 Fellowship of the Academy of American Poets.

Irving Feldman teaches at SUNY at Buffalo. He is finishing his third collection, *Cosmos and Other Poems,* which Viking will publish next year.

Edward Field attended New York University, has no degree, lists "various" past positions and "none at present." He has been traveling on the poetry-reading circuit. His two books of poems are *Stand Up, Friend, With Me* and *Variety Photoplays.*

William H. Gass's story "In the Heart of the Heart of the Country" appeared in *NAR #1* and "We Have Not Lived the Right Life," the opening section of his new novel, appeared in *NAR #6.* Mr. Gass has received a Guggenheim grant for next year and will be teaching philosophy at Washington University, St. Louis.

S. S. Gardons lives in Red Creek, Texas, where, he tells us, he was born, raised, and educated. He is the proprietor of a cycle shop and plays lead guitar with Chicken Gumbo, a local rock group.

Louise Glück attended Sarah Lawrence and is presently working as a secretary. *Firstborn,* her collection of poems several of which appeared in *NAR #1,* has created considerable interest in her work.

John Hollander's poems and articles have appeared in *The New Yorker, Harper's Magazine, Partisan Review,* and other journals. His fourth collection of poems, *Types of Shape,* has just been published. Mr. Hollander teaches English at City University of New York.

Michael Herr was the Vietnam correspondent for *Esquire* magazine in 1967–68. "Illumination Rounds" is taken from *Dispatches,* his book of reportage on Vietnam to be published this fall by Knopf.

Richard Howard's poem, "A Pre-Raphaelite Ending" will appear in a series of dramatic monologues, *Untitled Subjects,* based on Victorian writers, which will be published in September by Atheneum. Mr. Howard's study of contemporary American poets, *Alone With America,* will also be published this year.

Philip Levine has been living and traveling in Spain and Morocco this past year where he has finished two new books, one of poetry and one of poetry and graphics. Mr. Levine teaches creative writing at Fresno State College.

Lou Lipsitz has recently received a grant for his poetry from the National Endowment for the Arts. A political scientist, Mr. Lipsitz teaches at the University of North Carolina and is a member of the executive council of The Caucus For A New Political Science.

Kate Millett is a graduate of Oxford, a sculptor, and a members of the radical feminist movement as well as of the faculty of Barnard. Miss Millett's essay will appear in a somewhat expanded form as the opening chapter of her doctoral dissertation at Columbia, which Doubleday will publish next winter under the title *Sexual Politics*.

Henry H. Roth has published fiction in *Quest, December,* and other little magazines, and is working on a novel. He is not the author of *Call It Sleep*.

Hugh Seidman is working on a master's degree in Fine Arts at Columbia. His poetry has appeared in *Caterpillar, Intro, The Atlantic Monthly,* and elsewhere.

Mona Van Duyn's third volume of poems, *To See, To Take,* will be published by Atheneum early next year. Miss Van Duyn has been co-editor of *Perspective,* a literary quarterly, since it was founded in 1947.

William Crawford Woods has written for radio, television, and newspapers. He has also been a disc jockey and is presently the pop music critic for *The Washington Post.* He has published in *The Carolina Quarterly* and *Esquire,* and is currently writing a novel called *The Killing Zone*.

Diane Wakowski studied at the University of California and is presently teaching at the New School for Social Research. Her most recent collection of poetry is *Inside the Blood Factory* (Doubleday).

L. Woiwode's stories have appeared in *The New Yorker* and *Mademoiselle*. He is the author of *What I'm Going To Do, I Think,* one of the highly regarded first novels of this year.

James Wright teaches English at Hunter College. His volumes of poetry include *The Green Wall* (1957), *Saint Judas* (1959), *The Branch Will Not Break* (1963), and *Shall We Gather at the River* (1968).

Jay Wright lives in Mexico where he is writing plays and preparing his first collection of poetry. Mr. Wright has studied at the University of California, Union Theological Seminary, and Rutgers, and has been poet-in-residence at Tougaloo College.

David P. Young is editor of *Field*, a new journal of poetry and poetics from Oberlin. His first book of poems, *Sweating Out the Winter*, was published this year (U. of Pittsburgh Press).

rolled on under the night." And if New York eventually supplanted Boston, it was partly because its publishers and editors understood its ancillary role while Boston tried to become a culture unto itself.

All of which may now seem beside the point of our socio-literary realities. The situation in writing resembles so much what is happening in the society-at-large that any alternative sense of things may well be so much sand heaped before the tide. Even so, the ruling idea behind *NAR* is to develop a solidly national journal, rather than just another one that comes out of New York, chic and self-regarding, its pulse on the nation's finger. That we have not yet succeeded, the editors would be the first to admit. Too much of our material still comes from the agent/editor nexus that *Esquire* once referred to as "the red hot center" and too little from writers who need *NAR* for a hearing. We have tried to demonstrate the range of vital, articulate voices in American writing today, but *NAR* still sounds more like a chorus than a forum. We have hoped to branch out into diverse areas of cultural interest, but *NAR* is still more or less rooted in the terrain of literature and libertarian politics. We anticipated that, once begun, *NAR* would generate an abundance of suitable material, but so far it has received barely enough to fill three issues a year.

There is not much an editor can do about fiction and poetry except to create a decent home for them. The main problem is with essays, which is also the main area of editorial initiative. The usual procedure is to draw up a list of interesting topics and then to run through your list of writers until you find a particularly eligible candidate for each one. The trouble with this is the presumption that you always know what's interesting, that your superficial knowledge of most matters is somehow enlarged by editorial intuition. Thus, behind some of our more "topical"—and predictable—magazines lurks an editor's routinized megalomania. Another trouble with this policy is that you have to intervene in a writer's life with your initiatives and suggestions, and unless he has been waiting for just this opportunity, what you are likely to get today is a bright serviceable free-lance performance, more or less tailored to your image or else adaptable to your editing.

Having seen how this policy conspires at both ends to create narrowness and sameness in a magazine's pages, we have tried to follow the riskier but more interesting course of asking a writer we want to publish to act on his own initiative, to write the essay that he has been waiting to write, the one that most matters, and to write it, like a story or poem, to meet the exigent specifications of the dialogue that he has been conducting with himself. Of course, there is no one policy that will guarantee a steady flow of vital, articulate essays on diverse subjects, but after putting out seven issues we are still convinced this is the best way of encouraging it. The sense of full consciousness that such writing at its best gives off, of convictions that have been thought through and felt and meant, also provides the standard for selecting the pieces that come to us in other ways. Something of this notion seems to be getting through. In a recent review, Robie Macauley remarks that "with so much light, quick [journalistic] intelligence around, it is a good deal harder to write a truly honest, deeply intelligent (and probably more awkward) essay on the same subject. I think that this is what [*NAR*] is aiming for and . . . most of the time . . . succeeds in getting."

But not often enough and not variously enough. We have published little literary, art, or music criticism, nothing on science or philosophy, or history. And so forth. Which means that we haven't jogged enough writing arms, inquired into enough periodicals, fostered enough writerly feedback. Similarly, our fiction and poetry could stand more diversity, and we should do more about publishing plays. So we encourage submissions in all of these areas. We don't want to close our minds to the writers that we and the editor/agent network don't know about, we don't want to settle for the New York sense of what American writing is and where it's going. We want to keep the line of transmission open, to maintain *NAR* as an ongoing American question to which only its writers have the answers.

TS

SUBSCRIBE TO NEW AMERICAN REVIEW

As a charter subscriber you will receive the next four issues of New American Review at the special price of $4.00 instead of the regular cover price of $5.00.

As a special bonus, your subscription check or money order will bring you a free copy of NAR #1, 2, 3, 4, 5, or 6

If you'd like to reserve the next eight issues of New American Review you will save $3.00 and receive a free copy of NAR #1, 2, 3, 4, 5, or 6

The New American Review (Department NAL 6)
1937 Williamsbridge Road
Bronx, New York 10461

NAME _____

ADDRESS _____

CITY_____ STATE_____ ZIP_____

1. Enclosed is my check or money order for $4.00. Please start my subscription to the next four issues of New American Review, beginning with #7. Send my FREE copy of NAR #1 ☐ NAR #2 ☐ NAR #3 ☐ NAR #4 ☐ NAR #5 ☐ NAR #6 ☐   (Check one.)

2. Enclosed is my check or money order for $7.00. Please start my subscription to the next eight issues of New American Review, beginning with #7. Send my FREE copy of NAR #1 ☐ NAR #2 ☐ NAR #3 ☐ NAR #4 ☐ NAR #5 ☐ NAR #6 ☐   (Check one.)

You may also obtain the other NAR issues by enclosing the per issue price, plus 10¢ for handling and postage for each issue you want.
☐ NAR #1—$.95 ☐ NAR #2—$.95 ☐ NAR #3—$1.25 ☐ NAR #4—$1.25 ☐ NAR #5—$1.25 ☐ NAR #6—$1.25   (check one or more)

Offer good in U.S. and Canada only